SPHERICAL TRIGONOMETRY

An Introduction to
SPHERICAL TRIGONOMETRY

With practical examples, for students of
NAVIGATION, HYDROGRAPHIC SURVEYING
and NAUTICAL ASTRONOMY

BY

J. H. CLOUGH-SMITH

B.Sc. (Lond.), Extra-Master, F.R.I.N.,

formerly
Head of the Department of Maritime Studies,
University of Wales Institute of Science and Technology

GLASGOW
BROWN, SON & FERGUSON, LTD., NAUTICAL PUBLISHERS
52 DARNLEY STREET

First Printed 1966

Second Edition 1978

ISBN 0 85174 320 *X*

© 1978 Brown, Son & Ferguson, Ltd., Glasgow, G41 2SG

Made and Printed in Great Britain.

INTRODUCTION TO FIRST EDITION

The contents of this book are based on experience gained whilst teaching the subject in the Department of Maritime Studies in the Welsh College of Advanced Technology, later to become the University of Wales Institute of Science and Technology.

The scope of the book is not exhaustive, nor is any claim made to have evolved any new theory, discovered any new fact, although the treatment in many instances may be new, especially in those parts which deal with the solution of problems, and with the use of formulae in proving identities.

I am greatly indebted to works by Todhunter and Leathem, McLelland and Preston, Winter and others — a fuller list of acknowledgements is given at the end of the text.

Above all, perhaps, I should mention that splendid old textbook, Goodwin's *Plane and Spherical Trigonometry*. Indeed, it was largely because Goodwin has now been out of print for many years that I felt compelled to try and write something to take its place.

It is my hope, therefore, that this book will commend itself to teachers of navigational subjects at all levels and particularly to students working for qualifications at the highest standard available. At the present time, in the United Kingdom, this is represented by the Extra-Master's Certificate and this book should prove adequate for this purpose and for any other courses up to first degree standard.

In preparing the questions set in the text, I acknowledge with gratitude the inspiration provided by former questions set by the Ministry of Transport in their Extra-Masters' Examinations.

My thanks are due to all who have helped with this production, and especially to my colleague Captain F. G. Merrifield for his invaluable assistance in checking the manuscript. It is my sincere hope that not too many errors will have found their way into print, but I would be very grateful indeed to learn of any that may be discovered.

J. H. CLOUGH-SMITH,
CARDIFF.

INTRODUCTION TO SECOND EDITION

In all essentials the book remains substantially unchanged. The opportunity has been taken to tidy up a few inaccuracies in the text, in relation to which I am particularly grateful to friends and colleagues in the City of London Polytechnic, the Glasgow College of Nautical Studies, Plymouth Polytechnic and the University of Wales Institute of Science and Technology, not only for their help and advice but also for kindly allowing me to include a few additional examples selected from their recent examinations.

It is hoped that this revised edition will continue to make a useful contribution to courses in navigation and related subjects up to the highest level.

J. H. CLOUGH-SMITH,
EASINGWOLD, 1978

CONTENTS

BIBLIOGRAPHY and ACKNOWLEDGEMENTS

The Author acknowledges with gratitude his indebtedness to the following publications;—

Admiralty Manuals of Navigation, Vols. 2 and 3. H.M. Stationery Office.

Ageton, A. A. *Dead Reckoning and Azimuth Tables*, U.S. Hydrographic Office, (H.O. 211). First edition 1931.

Aquino, R. de *Log and Versine Altitude Tables*, London, 1924.
Sea and Air Navigation Tables (Log Tangents $\pm$ Log Secants).
Universal Nautical and Aeronautical Tables (Aquino's Tabular), Rio de Janeiro, 1943.

Burdwood, J. *Sun's True Bearing or Azimuth Tables (and others)*, J. D. Potter, London.

Burton, S. M. *Nautical Tables*, First edition 1936, London, Geo. Philip and Sons, Ltd.

Davis, P. L. H. *Alt-Azimuth Tables, (and others)*, J. D. Potter, London.

Dreisonstok, J. Y. *Navigation Tables for Mariners and Aviators*, U.S. Hydrographic Office (H.O. 208). First edition, 1929.

Gingrich, J. E. *Aerial and Marine Navigational Tables*, London, McGraw-Hill. First edition, 1931.*

Goodwin, H. B. *Plane and Spherical Trigonometry*, Longmans, Green and Co., London.*

Hughes, H. and Sons, Ltd. *Tables for Sea and Air Navigation*, London, 1938.

Inman, J. *Nautical Tables*, first published 1821, revised 1910, second edition 1918, London, J. D. Potter.

Lieuwen, J. C. *Short Method Navigation Tables using D.R. Positions*, first English Edition, 1951, London, Geo. Philip and Son, Ltd.
Record Tables, first English Edition, 1953. N.V. Observator, Rotterdam.

McClelland, W. J. and Preston, T. *A Treatise on Spherical Trigonometry*, Macmillian and Co., London.*

Myerscough, W. and Hamilton, W. *Rapid Navigation Tables*, London, Sir Isaac Pitman and Sons, Ltd. First edition, 1939.

Norie, J. W. *Nautical Tables*, London. Imray, Laurie, Norie and Wilson, Ltd.

Ogura, S. *New Altitude and Azimuth Tables for the Determination of the Position Line at Sea*, Tokyo, Nippon Yusen Kaisha. First English Edition, 1924.

Pierce, M. R. *Position Tables for Aerial and Surface Navigation*, U.S. Hydrographic Office (H.O. 209), 1931.

Smart, W. M. and Shearme, F. N. *Position Line Tables (Sine Method)*, London, J. D. Potter. First edition, 1922.

Sight Reduction Tables for Air Navigation (H.O. 249). A joint United States—United Kingdom production. (In the U.K., A.P. 3270.)

Tables of Computed Altitude and Azimuth (H.D. 486). A joint United States—United Kingdom production, published in the U.S. by the Hydrographic Office (H.O. 214).

Todhunter, I and Leathem, J. G. *Spherical Trigonometry*. Macmillan and Co., London.

Weems, P. V. H. *Air Navigation*, McGraw-Hill, Ltd., London.

Winter, W. P. *Trigonometry for Navigating Officers*, Sir Isaac Pitman and Sons, London.

Out of print.

CHAPTER I.

DEFINITIONS: GEOMETRICAL PROPERTIES OF THE SPHERE AND SPHERICAL TRIANGLES.

1. THE SPHERE.

Spherical trigonometry is concerned with the sphere and with spherical triangles.

A sphere is a figure such that all points of its surface are equally distant from a certain point within it, called the centre.

Any straight line drawn from the centre of the sphere to the surface is called a radius, and a straight line drawn through the centre and terminated both ways by the surface is called a diameter.

2. GREAT AND SMALL CIRCLES.

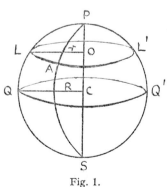

Fig. 1.

A **great circle** on the surface of a sphere is one whose plane passes through the centre of the sphere. For example, all meridians are great circles, and so is the Equator. A great circle divides the sphere into two equal parts.

A **small circle** is one whose plane does not pass through the centre of the sphere. A parallel of latitude, such as LL' is a small circle.

The angular distance, or arc, PL is called the **spherical radius** of the small circle LL', and P is called the **pole** of that small circle. Otherwise, the "radius of a small circle" is usually taken to mean OL (r).

The pole of a circle is that point on the surface of the sphere which is equidistant from all points on the circle.

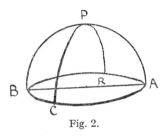

Fig. 2.

Hence P is also the pole of the great circle QQ', and clearly, the spherical radius of a great circle is a quadrant, that is 90°, i.e. PA, PC, PB are all equal to 90°, where ACB is a great circle.

Also it is clear that all great circles have two poles.

R is the radius of the sphere and is also the radius of every great circle.

The term **lune** is almost self-explanatory to those who have studied the changing appearance of the moon. However, by definition a lune is a portion of the surface of a sphere enclosed by two great circles. For instance, in fig 1, $PLQSAP$ is a lune, and $\angle LPA$ is the angle of the lune.

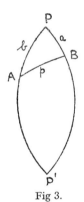

Fig 3.

Again, in the lune $PAP'BP$ (it will be appreciated that P and P' are at opposite ends of a diameter) if PAB is a spherical triangle, then $P'AB$ is called the **co-lunar triangle**.

Comparing the co-lunar triangle with triangle PAB, it is clear that they have a common side (p) and an equal angle $(\angle P = \angle P')$. The remaining sides and angles in the co-lunar triangle are the supplements of the corresponding parts in the triangle PAB.

3. LINE PERPENDICULAR TO A PLANE.

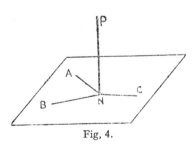

Fig, 4.

A straight line is perpendicular to a plane when it is perpendicular to every line meeting it in that plane; and conversely, if a straight line is perpendicular to a plane, it is perpendicular to every line lying in that plane and meeting it. E.g. PN, being perpendicular to the plane, makes right angles with NA, NB, NC.

4. ANGLE BETWEEN A LINE AND A PLANE.

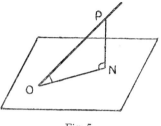

Fig. 5.

From any point P in the line drop a perpendicular to the plane, PN. Join ON.

The $\angle PON$ is the angle between the line and the plane.

5. ANGLE BETWEEN TWO PLANES.

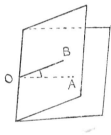

Fig. 6.

This is defined as the angle between BO and AO, where BO and AO lie one in each plane and are both normal (at right angles) to the line of intersection of the planes.

6. ANGLE BETWEEN PLANES OF TWO GREAT CIRCLES.

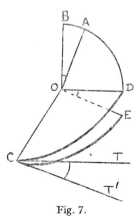

Fig. 7.

B is the pole of the great circle DC
A is the pole of the great circle EC.
BO is normal to the plane ODC.
AO is normal to the plane OEC.
DO and EO are both normal to the line of intersection of the planes, CO.

The angle between the planes, by para. 5, is $\angle EOD$ Also $\angle EOD = \angle BOA$.

Hence, the angle between the planes of two great circles can be defined as the **arc of a great circle between the poles of the two great circles whose planes we are considering.**

7. SPHERICAL ANGLE BETWEEN TWO GREAT CIRCLES.

This is defined as the angle between two tangents drawn to the point of intersection of the great circles.

i.e. $\angle TCT'$ is the spherical angle between the great circles at C, and clearly $\angle TCT'=$ angle between the planes, $\angle EOD$. (fig. 7.)

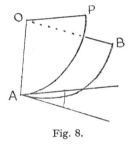

The above is quite general; in its simplest terms, the spherical angle $\angle PAB$ is defined as the angle between the tangents to the great circles drawn at the point of intersection. (fig. 8).

Fig. 8.

8. SPHERICAL TRIANGLE.

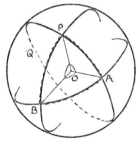

Fig. 9.

This is defined as a triangle formed on the surface of a sphere by the intersection of the **arcs of three great circles**: PAB is such a triangle. Note that the sides are formed only by arcs of great circles, never by small circles.

Similarly, a **spherical quadrilateral** is formed by the arcs of four great circles.

The arcs enclosing the spherical triangle are spoken of as its **sides**, and the angles in which these arcs intersect are the **angles** of the triangle. The three sides and three angles are collectively termed the **parts** of a spherical triangle, a term which is useful occasionally, since in reality all six are angles.

The angles have already been defined as the angle between the tangents.

The **length of side of a spherical triangle is defined as the angle subtended by that side at the centre of the sphere.** For example, length of side PB is $\angle POB$; side $PA=\angle POA$, and so on. Thus, the sides, like the angles, are expressed in degrees and minutes of arc (or of course, in radians).

If the actual length of the side is required (i.e. in feet, miles, etc.) this may easily be found knowing the radius of the sphere.

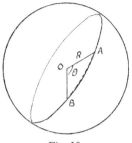

Fig. 10.

For example, if the length of side AB is 63° 18′, and the radius R of the sphere is 35 inches, then clearly length of whole great circle $=2\pi R=2\cdot\dfrac{.22}{7}\cdot 35=220$ inches.

And length of arc $AB=220\cdot\dfrac{63\cdot 3}{360}=\underline{38\cdot 7\text{ inches}}$

Alternatively (if θ is expressed in radians)

Length of arc, $AB,=R\times\theta=\dfrac{35\times 63\cdot 3}{57\cdot 3}=\dfrac{38\cdot 7\text{ inches}}{\text{as before.}}$

9. GREAT CIRCLE THROUGH TWO POINTS.

Through any two points* on the surface of a sphere one, and

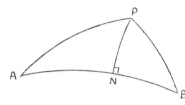

Fig. 11.

only one, great circle can be drawn. This enables us, for instance, in the triangle PAB, to use the words, "drop a perpendicular PN", with the knowledge that PN is still an arc of a great circle, since P and N are simply two points on the surface of the sphere and therefore there must exist a great circle to join them.

* (The exception to this rule occurs when the "two points" are at opposite ends of a diameter, such as the poles, in which case an infinite number of great circles can be drawn.)

10. SIZE OF A SPHERICAL TRIANGLE.

The "arc joining two points" is, by convention, always taken to mean the lesser segment of the great circle passing through the two points, i.e. in the triangle PAB (para. 8) by the "arc PA" we mean the obvious one, not PQA (which is still, within the terms of our definition, the "arc of a great circle joining the points".)

However, we always work with the lesser arc—in short, a side of a spherical triangle must be less than 180°. If we therefore imagine the triangle PAB (para. 8) expanding to its maximum possible size, it will be seen that in the limit, this would occur when

PAB completely occupied the hemisphere. The sum of the three sides would then equal 360°.

At the lower limit, the triangle may be considered as diminishing

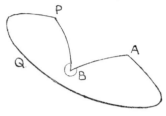

in size until the sides become very small indeed, in which case the sum of the three sides approaches zero.

By the same convention, by "the $\angle PBA$" is meant the smaller of the two angles at B in fig. 12, (i.e. not the angle defined by arc PQA). Thus, no angle of a spheri-

Fig. 12.

cal triangle can exceed 180°, and each of the three angles, in the limiting case when triangle PBA is imagined as just about to fill the hemisphere, will be 180° so that their sum will be 540°.

At the lower limit, when the triangle becomes very small indeed, it becomes virtually identical with a plane triangle, and the sum of its three angles equals 180°.

Summary.

1. *Each side of a spherical triangle is less than* 180°.
2. *Each angle of a spherical triangle is less than* 180°.
3. *The sum of the three sides must lie between* 0° *and* 360°.
4. *The sum of the three angles must lie between* 180° *and* 540°.
5. *The area of any spherical triangle must be less than* $2\pi R^2$.

11. PRIMARY AND SECONDARY CIRCLES.

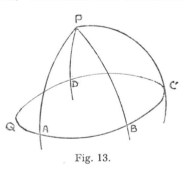

Fig. 13.

Any circle is called a **primary** in relation to those great circles which cut it at right angles.

These latter are called **secondaries**. E.g. PA, PB, PC, PD are secondaries to the great circle QC.

It is clear that all secondaries pass through the poles of the primary. For example, all meridians are secondaries to the Equator.

The distance of any point on the surface of a sphere from a circle traced on the sphere is measured by the arc of the secondary intercepted between the point and the circle; in other words, by the "distance" of a point from the arc of a great circle, we mean its perpendicular distance, expressed in arc.

12. TWO GREAT CIRCLES BISECT ONE ANOTHER.

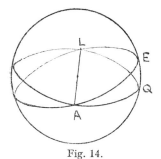

Fig. 14.

This is evident from the figure, and a line joining their points of intersection is a diameter.

In passing, let us note again that $AELQA$ is a lune (see para. 2).

13. THE EQUALITY OF TRIANGLES.

The proof of their equality, by superimposing one plane triangle on another, may be applied equally well to spherical triangles. Hence:—

Two triangles which are drawn on the same sphere, or on two spheres of equal radius, have all their corresponding elements equal if:—

  (a) *Two sides and the included angle in one are respectively equal to the two sides and included angle in the other.*

  (b) *Three sides in one are respectively equal to three sides in the other.*

  (c) *One side and the two adjacent angles in one are respectively equal to one side and the two adjacent angles in the other. (Or one side and any two angles, if one of them be a right angle.)*

  (d) *Three angles in one are respectively equal to three angles in the other.*

The first three may be proved by the method of superposition. The fourth, which has no counterpart in plane geometry, may be proved by consideration of the polar triangle (para. 25).

Two triangles which have their corresponding elements equal, as above, may be **congruent**, i.e. it may be possible to superimpose one on the other, or they may be **symmetrically equal**, which means that they cannot be superimposed because their curvatures are opposite.

For example:—If these two triangles are both convex towards the eye, they are symmetrically equal, not congruent.

14. SOME USEFUL GEOMETRICAL PROPERTIES.

The following geometrical properties of spherical triangles are closely analogous to their counterparts in plane geometry. They are stated here with the minimum of proof.

(a) **Any two sides of a spherical triangle are together greater than the third.**

Fig. 15.

Since by definition the great circle AB is the shortest distance between A and B, it follows that $AC+CB>AB$ (fig. 15).

(b) **The angles at the base of an isosceles triangle are equal.** A perpendicular from P on to AB bisects the base at right angles and also bisects the vertical angle.

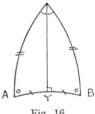

Fig. 16.

Proof as in plane geometry, by consideration of triangles PAY, PBY, using 13(b).

(c) **In any spherical triangle, the greater angle is opposite the greater side, and conversely.**

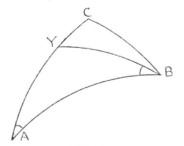

Fig. 17.

For, if $\angle B>\angle A$ (fig. 17), draw BY, making $\angle ABY=\angle A$. Then, by (b) $AY=BY$.
But $BY+CY>BC$; therefore $AC>BC$.

It follows from this, for example, that in any triangle ABC, $A-B$ and $a-b$ must be of the same sign . . . . N.B.

(d) **If in a spherical triangle, two sides are equal to each other, then the opposite angles are also equal to each other.**

This is evident from (b) and (c).

(e) **The great circles which are the internal bisectors of the angles (or two external and one internal) are concurrent.**

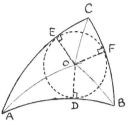

Fig. 18.

The point of concurrence, O, is the pole of the small circle touching the sides of the triangle. Hence, the perpendiculars from O on to the three sides are equal to each other.

Proof as in plano. Bisect $\angle A$ and $\angle C$ and let them meet in O. Join OB. All points on OA are equidistant from AC and AB, $\therefore$ $OD=OE$ and similarly $OE=OF$, $\therefore$ $OD=OF$, whence it easily follows that OB bisects $\angle B$, i.e. the three bisectors meet in O.

(f) **The great circles which bisect the sides of a triangle at right angles are concurrent.**

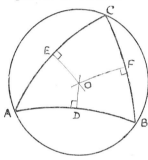

Fig. 19.

The point of concurrence is the pole of a small circle passing through the vertices of the triangle.

Hence $OC=OA=OB$.

Proof as in plano. Draw EO and FO at right angles through midpoints. From O drop OD perpendicular to AB. EO is locus of points equidistant from A and C, hence $OA=OC$. Similarly $OC=OB$. Therefore $OA=OB$ and since OD is dropped perpendicular to AB, it follows that D is the mid-point of AB.

(g) **The great circle bisecting any two sides of a triangle intersects the third side produced at a point 90° from the mid-point of the third side.**

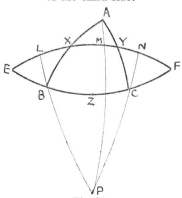

Fig. 20.

Let ABC be the triangle, X, Y, Z the mid-points, the great circle through X and Y meeting BC produced in E and F. We have to show that $EZ=FZ=90°$.

Let BL, AM, CN be secondaries drawn through the vertices of the triangle to the great circle EXF. P is the pole of EXF. It can easily be shown that triangles BLX, AMX are equal, and so $BL=AM$. Similarly $CN=AM$.

Hence it may be shown that triangles BLE, CNF are equal, so $BE=CF$ and so $EZ=FZ=90°$.

(*h*)   **The perpendiculars from the vertices of a spherical triangle on to the opposite sides are concurrent.**

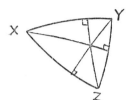

This follows from (*g*), for, if XYZ is the triangle, since $FZ=90°$, the perpendicular from Z on to XY will also be at right angles to BC.

Similarly, the perpendicular from Y on to XZ is at right angles to AC, and from X on to YZ, is at right angles to AB.

Since these three perpendiculars from X, Y, Z are drawn through the mid-points of their respective sides BC, AC, AB and are at right angles to those sides, they are, by (*f*) concurrent.

(*j*)   **The great circles joining the vertices of a triangle to the mid-points of the opposite sides are concurrent.**

The proof of this last one is dealt with in para. 48, example 7.

CHAPTER II

FORMULAE—PRACTICAL APPLICATION IN SOLUTION OF TRIANGLES

Important Note:—

The attention of all readers is drawn to the Appendix, page 111, where a summary of formulae of plane trigonometry may be found.

These are referred to in the text which follows, as for example, " A. 12," meaning Appendix, formula 12.

15. THE COSINE FORMULA.

This is sometimes called the "fundamental formula" because so many formulae in spherical trigonometry are derived from it.

It states that in any spherical triangle,

$$\cos a = \cos b \cos c + \sin b \sin c \cos A$$

(The formula should be memorized in this form).

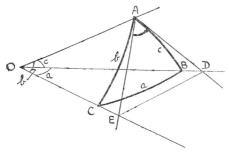

Proof: Let the triangle $A B C$ be as shown, O the centre of the sphere.

Sides a, b, c, are measured by the angles at the centre of the sphere, as indicated.

Fig 21.

AE, AD are perpendicular to OA, and $\angle EAD = \angle A$.

In the plane triangle AED (by cosine formula   .... A. 12)

$$DE^2 = AE^2 + AD^2 - 2AE.AD \cos A \quad \dots \quad \dots \quad \dots \quad (1)$$

and in triangle OED,

$$DE^2 = OE^2 + OD^2 - 2OE.OD \cos a \quad \dots \quad \dots \quad \dots \quad (2)$$

Also, $OE^2 = AE^2 + OA^2$ and $OD^2 = AD^2 + OA^2$ so that (2) becomes

$$DE^2 = 2OA^2 + AE^2 + AD^2 - 2OE.OD \cos a \quad \dots \quad \dots \quad (3)$$

and equating (1) and (3).

11

$$2OA^2 - 2OE.OD \cos a = -2AE.AD \cos A \qquad \dots \qquad \dots \qquad (4)$$
$$OE.OD \cos a = OA^2 + AE.AD \cos A$$
$$\cos a = \frac{OA.OA}{OE \ OD} + \frac{AE.AD}{OE \ OD} \cdot \cos A$$

i.e.   **cos a = cos b cos c + sin b sin c cos A**

It follows without further proof that

cos b = cos c cos a + sin c sin a cos B

cos c = cos a cos b + sin a sin b cos C

.. I

NOTE:

The above is the usual proof of the cosine formula. It does assume that the two sides including the given angle, AB and AC, are both less than 90° (Since if they were not, the tangents AD and AE would never intersect OB and OC produced.)

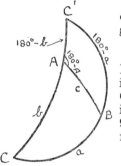

Fig. 22.

If required, it may easily be extended to cover the case when one or both sides is greater than 90°.

For example, let AC be greater than 90°.

Produce CA and CB until they intersect. Let this be at C'. Then $C'ACBC'$ is a lune, in which the parts are as shown (see para. 2). Considering the $\angle C'AB$, the two sides which include it, AC' and AB, are both less than 90°, and therefore we may write, by cosine formula,

$\cos \ (180° - a)$

$= \cos \ c \ \cos \ (180° - b) + \sin \ c \ \sin \ (180° - b) \ \cos \ (180° - A)$

$- \cos a = \cos c. - \cos b + \sin c \sin b. - \cos A$

i.e. $\cos a = \cos b \cos c + \sin b \sin c \cos A$

as before.

If both AB and AC are greater than 90°, by producing both AB and AC to form a lune, a similar proof is easily deduced.

Hence, the cosine formula holds good for all values of the parts used, up to 180°.

16. The cosine formula may be used (and is used, sometimes) in the solution of a spherical triangle, especially by those whose logarithmic tables do not contain versines or haversines.

In the form stated at I, it may be used, given two sides and the included angle, to find the third side.

By transposing the formula, we get

$$\cos A = \frac{\cos a - \cos b \cos c}{\sin b \sin c} \qquad .. \qquad .. \qquad .. \qquad II$$

a form in which it may be used, given three sides, to find any angle.

However, it is not ideal for logarithmic work, partly because of the existence of the $+$ or $-$ signs, and secondly, because the cosine of an angle between 90° and 180° is negative.

In the reduction of sights by routine solution of the astronomical triangle, it is desirable to avoid these complications if possible, and this is done by the use of versines or haversines.

17. THE NATURAL HAVERSINE FORMULA.

By definition, versine $A = 1 - \cos A$ and so "haversine" A, being "half the versine", is given by hav $A = \frac{1}{2}(1 - \cos A)$.

The haversine of an angle is thus always positive, and it increases from 0 to 1 as the angle increases from 0° to 180°.

To derive the haversine formula:—

Given $\cos a = \cos b \cos c + \sin b \sin c \cos A$ ....   (1)
and from above, $\cos A = 1 - 2$ hav A

and of course $\cos a = 1 - 2$ hav a, we have, substituting in (1).

$1 - 2$ hav $a = \cos b \cos c + \sin b \sin c \ (1 - 2$ hav $A)$

$1 - 2$ hav $a = \cos b \cos c + \sin b \sin c - 2 \sin b \sin c$ hav A

$1 - 2$ hav $a = \cos (b \sim c) - 2 \sin b \sin c$ hav A ....   (using A 5.)

and since $\cos (b \sim c) = 1 - 2$ hav $(b \sim c)$,

$1 - 2$ hav $a = 1 - 2$ hav $(b \sim c) - 2 \sin b \sin c$ hav A.

$$\text{hav } a = \text{hav } (b \sim c) + \sin b \sin c \text{ hav } A \qquad .. \qquad III$$

This is the haversine formula, sometimes called the **natural haversine formula,** to distinguish it from its logarithmic counterpart. It is used in the solution of a wide variety of navigational problems.

In this form, it may be used,
given two sides and the included angle, to find the third side.

By transposing, we get

$$\text{hav } A = \frac{\text{hav } a - \text{hav } (b \sim c)}{\sin b \sin c} \qquad .. \qquad .. \qquad .. \qquad IV$$

a form in which it may be used,
given three sides, to find any angle.

In both forms, therefore, it may be used in preference to the cosine formula.

It should be noted :—

(a) that the term sin b sin c hav A is always less than unity. This simplifies the taking out of its anti-logarithm, especially since tables of haversines employed in navigational work usually have the natural values and their logarithms tabulated side by side.

(b) that sin b is a number, sin c is a number, and therefore sin b sin c hav A may be regarded as a haversine multiplied by a number, that is, still a haversine. Hence, there will always be some angle θ, such that

hav θ=some number $\times$ hav A.

Since the "number" in question is sin b sin c, we may write:

hav θ=sin b sin c hav A.

Although perhaps not very important, this does explain why,

when we add:—log sin b
log sin c
log hav A
_____

we sometimes write → log hav
_____

The purist may ask, "What is it the log hav of?"—and the answer is that it is the log hav of this imaginary angle θ. It is most convenient to call it a "log hav" because, as already mentioned, the haversine tables have natural values and their logarithms side by side.

Since in reality it is simply a logarithm, and we want its anti-logarithm, the easiest way of doing this is by the haversine table.

(c) that although we still have the presence of plus and minus signs, these only require one single change from logarithms to natural values whereas in the cosine formula the change has to be made twice. A little practice in their use will make this clear.

(d) that the difference sign, $b{\sim}c$, is taken to mean $b-c$ or $c-b$, whichever gives a $+ve$ value.

18. Students whose tables do not contain haversines will find the following alternative form useful.

Given the cosine formula,

$$\cos a = \cos b \cos c + \sin b \sin c \cos A \quad \dots \quad \dots \quad \dots \quad (1)$$

since $2 \sin^2 \dfrac{A}{2} = 1 - \cos A \quad \dots \quad \dots \quad \dots$ (see A 11)

$$\cos A = 1 - 2 \sin^2 \dfrac{A}{2}$$

and substituting in (1)

$$\cos a = \cos b \cos c + \sin b \sin c \left(1 - 2 \sin^2 \dfrac{A}{2}\,\right)$$

and using $A. 5$,

$$\cos a = \cos (b \smallfrown c) - 2 \sin b \sin c \sin^2 \frac{A}{2} \qquad .. \qquad V$$

The logarithmic computation in this is somewhat easier than in the cosine formula, but it is still not as good as *III* or *IV*, when haversines are available.

19.   THE SINE FORMULA.

This states that in any spherical triangle,

$$\frac{\sin a}{\sin A} = \frac{\sin b}{\sin B} = \frac{\sin c}{\sin C} \qquad .. \qquad .. \qquad .. \qquad VI$$

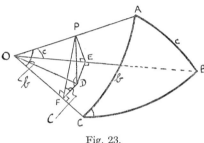

Fig. 23.

Proof:

Let *ABC* be a spherical triangle, and *O* the centre of the sphere.

Let *P* be any point on *OA*.

From *P*, drop perpendicular *PD* to the plane *OBC*.

Drop *DF*, *DE*, perpendiculars to *OC*, *OB*.

Join *PF*, *PE*, *OD*.

Then $\angle PDF$, $\angle PDE$, $\angle PDO$ are all right angles, and by construction $\angle DFO$, $\angle DEO$ are also right angles.

To show that $\angle PFO$ is also a right angle, we have
$$PF^2 = PD^2 + DF^2$$
$$= PO^2 - OD^2 + OD^2 - OF^2$$

i.e. $PF^2 = PO^2 - OF^2$, $\therefore$ triangle *PFO* is right angled at *F*.

Similarly, triangle *PEO* is right angled at *E*.

We now have, $PF = PO \sin b$
and also $PD = PF \sin C$
$$= PO \sin b \sin C \qquad .... \qquad .... \qquad .... \qquad (1)$$

Similarly, $PE = PO \sin c$
and $PD = PE \sin B$
$$= PO \sin c \sin B.... \qquad .... \qquad .... \qquad .... \qquad (2)$$

Equating (1) and (2)
$$\sin b \sin C = \sin c \sin B$$

i.e. $\dfrac{\sin b}{\sin B} = \dfrac{\sin c}{\sin C}$

Similarly, by dropping a perpendicular from a point in OB on to plane OAC, it may be shown that $\dfrac{\sin a}{\sin A} = \dfrac{\sin c}{\sin C}$

Hence $$\frac{\sin a}{\sin A} = \frac{\sin b}{\sin B} = \frac{\sin c}{\sin C} \quad .. \quad (3)$$

20. The great advantage of the sine formula is its beautiful simplicity—simple both to remember and to use. Note that it gives the relation between two angles and the two sides opposite to them. Given any three of these parts, the fourth may be found.

Its big disadvantage is the **ambiguity** about the actual value of the part found, since $\sin A = \sin (180° - A)$. In short, when we have performed our logarithmic computation and taken out the anti-log of our log sine and obtained (say) $42°$, the question arises—is the answer $42°$ or $138°$? They both have the same log sine.

This difficulty arises whenever an angle is found through its sine. There will sometimes be two solutions, sometimes one, and some-times no solution at all. Disregarding the third rather theoretical possibility, some progress can be made on the first two by remember-ing that, in any triangle, $A - B$ and $a - b$ must be of the same sign (para. 14c).

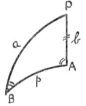

Consider a practical example, a triangle PAB as shown, in which $b = 26° 21'$

$\qquad B = 52° 22'$

$\qquad A = 104° 44'$

To find a, we have

$$\frac{\sin a}{\sin A} = \frac{\sin b}{\sin B}$$

	9·64724
	9·98548
	10·10131
log sin	9·73403

$\sin a = \sin b \sin A \operatorname{cosec} B$ log sin
and de-logging, $a = 32° 50'$.

Is it $32° 50'$ or $147° 10'$? $A - B$ is $+ve$, and so $a - b$ must also be $+ve$. But both values for a satisfy this requirement; thus both are solutions of the data as given, and from the practical point of view we are not much further ahead.

This ambiguity always exists, and sometimes (but only some-times) can it be resolved by applying the above rule.

On the other hand, in a practical problem, there may be some physical fact (such as, a latitude must be less than $90°$; the sun's declination cannot exceed 23° 28', and so on)—there may be some fundamental fact in the problem which enables us to know within what range of values our answer must lie. In such a case, there is no doubt that the sine formula is very quick and easy to use—and it should be used.

But if it is just a case of some quite unknown "triangle ABC", it is better to avoid the sine formula if this is possible. If it is not possible, we must be prepared for either two solutions, or one solution, as a result of applying the test mentioned above, namely, that if A is greater than B, then a must be greater than b.

21. THE AMBIGUOUS CASE WHEN THERE ARE TWO TRIANGLES.

Quite apart from the ambiguity which may arise in the value of an angle when found through its sine, it can occasionally happen that there are, in fact, two triangles which may be constructed with the data available.

Doubtless readers will recall the similar case in plane geometry and, though not exact, the analogy is sufficiently close to illustrate the principles involved.

Let us consider a triangle ABC in which we are given A, b and a ($a<b$).

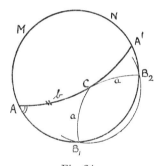

Fig. 24

Let ANM be any great circle. At any point A construct the angle A, and let $AC=b$. With arc equal to a, strike in B_1 and B_2.

Then clearly, both AB_1C and AB_2C comply with the data given. Hence, there are, in fact, two triangles. This is the ambiguous case. It occurs—sometimes, not always—when the smaller side given is opposite the given angle.

The qualifying words inserted are necessary since the two positions, B_1 and B_2, must satisfy the restriction contained in the definition of a spherical triangle (that no side shall exceed 180°). Since two great circles bisect each other (para. 12) arc $AB_2A'=180°$, and thus for two triangles to be formed, B_2 must not fall beyond A'.

Though this ambiguous triangle only occurs very seldom, it is liable to lead to difficulties unless it is recognized on the rare occasions when it does occur.

22. THE FOUR-PART FORMULA.

This states that, in a spherical triangle ABC,

$$\cot a \sin b = \cot A \sin C + \cos b \cos C \quad .. \quad VII$$

C

It should be memorized in this form.

Proof:

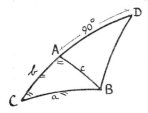

Produce CA to D making $AD = 90°$.
Join DB.

Fig. 25.

In the $\triangle BCD$. By cosine formula,

$$\cos C = \frac{\cos BD - \cos (90° + b)\cos a}{\sin (90° + b) \sin a}$$

$$= \frac{\cos BD + \sin b \cos a}{\cos b \sin a}$$

and $\cos BD = \cos b \sin a \cos C - \sin b \cos a$ .... (1)

In the $\triangle ABD$.

$$\cos (180° - A) = \frac{\cos BD - \cos 90° \cos c}{\sin 90° \sin c}$$

$$-\cos A = \frac{\cos BD}{\sin c} \quad \text{(since } \cos 90° = 0 \text{ and } \sin 90° = 1\text{)}$$

and $\cos BD = -\cos A \sin c$ .... (2)

Equating (1) and (2)

$$\cos b \sin a \cos C - \sin b \cos a = -\cos A \sin c$$
$$\cos a \sin b = \cos A \sin c + \cos b \sin a \cos C$$

Dividing by $\sin a$

$$\cot a \sin b = \frac{\cos A \sin c}{\sin a} + \cos b \cos C$$

By sine formula, $\dfrac{\sin c}{\sin a} = \dfrac{\sin C}{\sin A}$

whence, **$\cot a \sin b = \cot A \sin C + \cos b \cos C$**

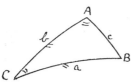

Note that the four parts used are all next to one another as we go round the triangle. Thus, knowing any three, we can find the fourth. (In practice it is always best to make the unknown part one of the **outer** parts, if possible.)

Whichever way we try to arrange these four parts, they must begin with a side and finish with an angle, one way or the other. These two may be referred to as the **outer** parts; the other two are obviously the inner parts. This leads to the following useful aid to the memory. It is quoted as it should be learned—and with apologies for the grammar!

"Cot outer side × sine inner side = cot outer angle × sine inner angle + product cosines of two inners."

. . .   .   N.B.

(The reader may note that there is an association of ideas between "cot" and "outer" and between "sine" and "inner" which helps the memory.)

23. Before concluding this chapter, we shall give one or two practical examples in order to fix ideas on the use of some of the preceding formulae.

Example 1. In a triangle PAB, in which P is the Pole and A, B, two places in the northern hemisphere, given $\angle A = 68°\ 00'$, $AB = 60°\ 30'$, $\angle P = 80°\ 16'$, find latitude of B.

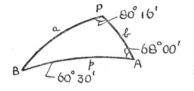

Find side a by sine formula. (This will be quite in order, since we know that B is in the northern hemisphere.)

$$\frac{\sin a}{\sin A} = \frac{\sin p}{\sin P}$$

$$\sin a = \sin p \sin A \operatorname{cosec} P$$

log sin p	9·93970
log sin A	9·96717
log cosec P	10·00630
log sin a	9·91317

$a = 54°\ 58'$ and Lat. $B = 35°\ 02'$ N.

Note that P is greater than A, and therefore p must be greater than a. Since p is $60°\ 30'$, the only possible value for a is $54°\ 58'$ (not $125°\ 02'$). In this case, the rule is confirmed by what we already know from the physical facts of the problem.

Example 2.

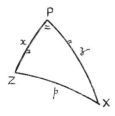

In a triangle PZX, given $\angle P = 50°\ 00'$, $z = 70°\ 45'$, $x = 62°\ 10'$, find p and $\angle Z$.

i.e. Two sides and the included angle, so use haversine formula to find p.

hav p=hav $(z-x)$+sin z sin x hav P

$z-x=8°\ 35'$

log sin z	9·97501
log sin x	9·94660
log hav P	9·25190

$p=46°\ 19'·5.$

log hav θ	9·17351
nat hav θ	·14911
nat hav $(z-x)$	·00560
nat hav p	·15471

We now have three sides, so use haversine formula to find $\angle Z$.

$$\text{hav } Z=\frac{\text{hav } z-\text{hav } (p\smallsmile x)}{\sin p \sin x}$$

nat hav z	·33515
nat hav $(x-p)$	·01899

$x-p=15°\ 50'·5$

nat hav	·31616

$\angle Z=89°\ 21'.$

log hav	9·49991
log cosec p	10·14070
log cosec x	10·05340
log hav Z	9·69401

Example 3. In the triangle PZX, give $\angle P=50°\ 00'$, $z=70°\ 45'$, $x=62°\ 10'$, find p without using haversines.

We shall use formula V.

$$\cos p=\cos (z\smallsmile x)-2 \sin z \sin x \sin^2 \frac{P}{2}$$

$z-x=8°\ 35'$

log sin$\frac{P}{2}$	9·62595
$\times 2$	9·25190
log sin x	9·94660
log sin z	9·97501
log 2	·30103
	9·47454
anti-log	·29823
nat cos $(z-x)$	·98880
nat cos p	·69057

$p=46°\ 19'·5$ as beore.

Example 4.

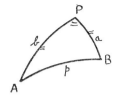

In a triangle PAB, $\angle P = 66° \ 30'$

$a = 47° \ 00'$, $b = 67° \ 00'$, find $\angle A$.

We shall use the four-part formula. (*Note that the unknown is an outer; this is always best. It is more difficult if the unknown is an inner.*)

$$\cot a \sin b = \cot A \sin P + \cos b \cos P$$

i.e. $\cot A = \dfrac{\cot a \sin b - \cos b \cos P}{\sin P}$

$$= \cot a \sin b \ \operatorname{cosec} P - \cos b \cot P$$

log cot a	9·96966	log cos b	9·59188
log sin b	9·96403	log cot P	9·63830
log cosec P	10·03760		
	9·97129		9·23018
anti-log	·93603		
	·16989	anti-log	·16989
cot A	·76614		
and $\angle A =$	52° 32'·5		

24. THE POLAR TRIANGLE.

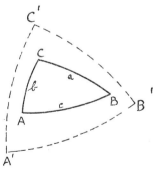

Fig. 26.

By the pole of a great circle we mean the point that is 90° distant from every point on the great circle.

Let ABC be a spherical triangle in which sides a, b, c are parts of the great circles suggested by their respective curvatures.

Let A' be the pole of the great circle which includes a

Let B' be the pole of the great circle which includes b

Let C' be the pole of the great circle which includes c

Then $A'B'C'$ is called the polar triangle of ABC, and ABC is called the primitive triangle.

Note that since every great circle has two poles, a series of such triangles might be formed by joining the poles in different ways. By convention, the poles chosen must lie on the same side of the arc as the opposite angle. For instance, A' lies in the same direction from arc a as does A, and so do B' and B, and C' and C, in relation to their respective arcs.

This is the only triangle which is referred to as the polar triangle.

If $A'B'C'$ is the polar triangle of ABC, then it can be shown that ABC is the polar triangle of $A'B'C'$.

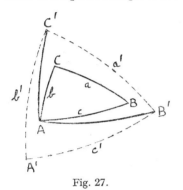

Fig. 27.

Let A' lie upon the same side of BC (arc a) as A.

Then if A' is the pole of arc a, we can show that A is the pole of arc a'.

Proof:

    Join AC', AB'.

    Since B' is the pole of AC, then AB' is a quadrant.

    Since C' is the pole of AB, then AC' is a quadrant.

Hence, since both AC' and AB' are quadrants, it follows that A is the pole of arc a'.

Similarly B is the pole of b' and C is the pole of c'.

(The reader will appreciate that it is not always easy to visualise where the polar triangle lies, or what it really looks like. We shall see later that it is quite unnecessary to do so. It is enough to know that it exists.)

25. THE SUPPLEMENTAL THEOREM.

This is a very important theorem relating to polar triangles. It states that:—

The angles in the polar triangle are supplements of the corresponding sides in the primitive triangle, and the sides in the polar triangle are supplements of the corresponding angles in the primitive triangle.

NOTE: "Corresponding" in the sense that we call b the side in the primitive corresponding to B' in the polar, and so on.

Hence, the supplemental theorem states that:
$B'=180°-b$; $a=180°-A'$; or in radians, $c'=\pi-C$, and so on.

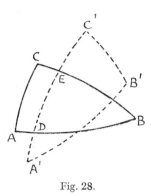

Fig. 28.

Proof:

Let side $A'C'$ intersect BA and BC in D and E respectively.

Since B is the pole of $A'C'$, i.e. the pole of DE, both BD and BE are quadrants and so arc $DE=\angle B$.

Since A' is the pole of BC, then $A'E$ is a quadrant.

Since C' is the pole of AB, then $C'D$ is a quadrant.

$\therefore C'D+A'E=180°$.

i.e. $A'C'+DE=180°$ and so $A'C'+\angle B=180°$

$\therefore \angle B$ and side $A'C'$ (i.e. b') are supplements.

Similarly it may be shown that A and a', C and c' are supplements.

26. This theorem has an important result, namely, *that any formula which holds good for any spherical triangle ABC will hold good when we substitute supplements of sides for angles and supplements of angles for sides.*

We shall return to the more theoretical aspects of this in a later chapter, but for the present, let us consider its practical application. This principle enables us to solve triangles which otherwise might require the use of more cumbersome formulae.

NOTE: It is not necessary to draw or try to visualize where the polar triangle is. It is essential however to adhere to the above notation.

Example 5.

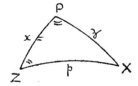

In a triangle PZX, given
$$x= 55°\ 14'$$
$$P= 54°\ 01'$$
$$Z=121°\ 25',$$
solve.

As it stands, two angles and included side.

So, in the polar triangle,

$X'=124°\ 46'$, $p'=125°\ 59'$	log hav	9·89493
$z'=58°\ 35'$, $p'\smallsmile z'=67°\ 24'$	log sin	9·93115
(two sides and included angle)	log sin	9·90805
	log	9·73413

So hav $x'=$ hav X' sin p' sin $z'+$ hav $(p'\smallsmile z')$	nat	·54217
$x'=134°\ 26'$	nat hav	·30785
	nat hav x'	·85002

and so $\underline{X=45°\ 34'}$.

Thus we have found a part in the primitive by solving the polar triangle. This is a very powerful method and should be understood. Some examples for practice follow.

EXERCISE 1—Solution of oblique triangles.

Formulae to be used are those given in this chapter, chiefly haversine formula (or V in lieu) with sine formula when there is no ambiguity and occasionally four-part formula, together with the ability to go into the polar triangle when necessary.

If four-figure logs are used, answers should be correct within about 3' of arc.

Solve the following spherical triangles:—

1. *PAB*, given $a=57°\ 00'$, $B=94°\ 01'$, $P=71°\ 51'·5$
   find b and p.
2. *PZX*, given $P=63°\ 47'·5$, $Z=83°\ 56'·5$, $X=93°\ 34'$,
   find p and z.
3. *PZY*, given $Z=70°\ 27'$, $P=114°\ 54'$, $Y=109°\ 42'$,
   find p and z.
4. *PZX*, given $p=87°\ 10'$, $z=62°\ 37'$, $x=100°\ 10'$,
   find P and Z.
5. *PZX*, given $P=88°\ 24'·5$, $z=98°\ 10'$, $x=100°\ 09'$,
   find p and Z.
6. *PAB*, given $A=33°\ 14'$, $a=80°\ 05'$, $b=70°\ 12'$,
   find B.
7. *PZX*, given $P=51°\ 30'$, $Z=113°\ 30'$, $PZ=60°\ 20'$,
   find PX and ZX.
8. *ABC*, given $a=49°\ 08'$, $C=71°\ 20'$, $b=58°\ 23'$,
   find A and B.
9. *PZX*, given $P=85°\ 30'$, $PZ=49°\ 34'$, $PX=99°\ 58'$,
   find Z.
10. *ABC*, given $A=88°\ 36'$, $B=121°\ 36'$, $C=69°\ 35'$,
    find a and b.

CHAPTER III

RIGHT ANGLED AND QUADRANTAL TRIANGLES

27. If a spherical triangle has one of its angles equal to 90° it is called a right angled triangle and if it has one of its sides equal to 90° that is to say, a quadrant, it is said to be a quadrantal triangle.

In such circumstances, the solution of the triangle becomes a much simpler matter.

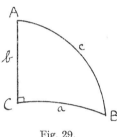

Fig. 29.

Consider the spherical triangle ABC, in which $\angle C = 90°$, and let us select formulae which include $\angle C$.

For instance, by the cosine formula, $\cos c = \cos a \cos b + \sin a \sin b \cos C$, which, since $\cos 90° = 0$, becomes $\cos c = \cos a \cos b$ ... ... (1)

Or by the four-part formula:—

$\cot a \sin b = \cot A \sin C + \cos b \cos C$, which since $\sin 90° = 1$, becomes $\cot a \sin b = \cot A$ ... (2)

Or again,

$\cot b \sin a = \cot B \sin C + \cos a \cos C$, which becomes $\cot b \sin a = \cot B$ ... ... (3)

It will be noted that none of these three formulae we have derived contains the right angle, C.

And in fact, we could proceed, if we wished, on similar lines and ultimately derive ten such formulae, all giving various relationships between the five parts b, A, c, B, a, and none of them involving C, the right angle.

These formulae may also be derived independently, as follows:—

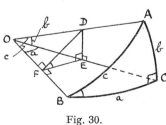

Fig. 30.

Let ABC be a triangle right angled at C, and O the centre of the sphere.

From any point D in OA drop perpendicular DE on to OC, and from E, draw EF perpendicular to OB. Join DF.

Since the plane AOC is perpendicular to the plane BOC, it follows that DE is perpendicular to EF. Hence,

$$DF^2 = DE^2 + EF^2 = OD^2 - OE^2 + OE^2 - OF^2$$

25

$DF^2=OD^2-OF^2$, therefore $\angle OFD$ is a right angle, and so $\angle DFE$ represents the inclination of the planes AOB and COB, that is, it represents the $\angle B$, i.e. $\angle DFE = \angle B$.

Thus, for example,

$$\cos c = \frac{OF}{OD} = \frac{OF}{OE} \cdot \frac{OE}{OD} = \cos a \cos b \ .... \qquad .... \qquad .... \qquad (1)$$

Or again,

$$\sin b = \frac{DE}{OD} = \frac{DE}{FD} \cdot \frac{FD}{OD} = \sin B \sin c$$

By a similar construction,
$$\sin a = \sin A \sin c$$

$$\left. \right\} \qquad ..... \qquad ...... \qquad .... \qquad (2)$$

Again,

$$\sin a = \frac{EF}{OE} = \frac{EF}{DE} \cdot \frac{DE}{OE} = \cot B \tan b$$

and similarly $\sin b = \cot A \tan a$

$$\left. \right\} \qquad .... \qquad .... \qquad .... \qquad (3)$$

Again,

$$\cos B = \frac{EF}{DF} = \frac{EF}{OF} \cdot \frac{OF}{DF} = \tan a \cot c$$

and similarly, $\cos A = \tan b \cot c$

$$\left. \right\} \qquad .... \qquad .... \qquad .... \qquad (4)$$

From these fundamental forms, obtained direct from the triangle, all others may be derived. For instance, multiplying the two formulae in (3) we get

$$\sin a \sin b = \cot A \tan B \tan a \tan b$$

whence $\cos a \cos b = \cot A \cot B$ and from (1),

$$\cos c = \cot A \cot B \qquad .... \qquad .... \qquad .... \qquad .... \qquad (5)$$

It is clear that we could go on for some time deriving similar formulae. They are numerous (ten in all) and not very easy to remember. Fortunately, we are not called upon to do so, since all the formulae can, with a little practice, be written down at sight direct from the triangle by the application of two rules, named after their discoverer, Napier's Rules of Circular Parts.

28. NAPIER'S RULES.

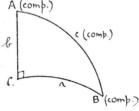

Fig. 31.

It has already been noted that the right angle does not appear in the final formulae and in using Napier's Rules, we ignore the presence of the right angle completely. This leaves five parts, b, A, c, B, a.

Of these parts, b and A for instance, are spoken of as being "next to each other"; B and c are next to each other, and so are a and b (since the presence of the right angle is ignored).

Given any two parts, we can find any third. Let us focus our attention therefore on these three parts we are working with i.e. two given and one to be found.

If all three are next to each other, the one in the middle is called the "middle part", and those on each side of it are called the "adjacent parts".

If two are next to each other and one is on its own, the latter is treated as the "middle part" and the other two are said to be "opposite" to it.

With these conventions, Napier's Rules are usually stated as follows:—

sine middle part = product of tangents of adjacent parts

and

sine middle part = product of cosines of opposite parts ... ... *N.B.*

(The a's in tangent and adjacent, and the o's in cosines and opposite.')

There is one final point to be noted, namely, that in writing down the equations by means of these rules, the two parts next to the right angle are written down as they are, the others (away from the right angle) **are written down as complements**, i.e. cos a, tan b etc., but tan complement A i.e. cot A, sin complement c i.e. cos c, and so on.

29. PRACTICE IN USING NAPIER'S RULES.

NOTE: We have not marked the parts A, b, C with the word "comp.", as we did in para. 28, because in practice, this is not done by an experienced operator—and in this paragraph we are trying to show how an experienced operator works. The beginner may find it helpful to do so.

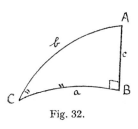

Fig. 32.

Now let us practise writing the equations down, using triangle ABC, in which we are given C and a. Note that B is now the right angle.

Find c.

Studying the three parts we are working with C, a, c, all three are next to each other. Therefore (sin mid. part = product tangents of adjacents)

$$\sin a = \tan c \cot C$$

The reader should aim at being able to write this equation down just like this, straight from the triangle.

The next step is to transpose it, and clearly,

$$\tan c = \sin a \tan C \quad \dots \quad \dots \quad \dots \quad (1)$$

Find A (still using a and C).

Again studying the three parts, A is on its own, the other two are next to each other. Hence

(sin mid. part=product cosines of opposites)

$$\cos A = \cos a \sin C \quad \dots \quad \dots \quad \dots \quad (2)$$

(This time the equation does not require transposing.)

Find b (still using a and C).

$$\cos C = \tan a \cot b.$$

(This is the equation that matters. The reader should by now see how it is written down, straight from the triangle.)

And transposing,

$$\cot b = \cos C \cot a \quad \dots \quad \dots \quad \dots \quad (3)$$

30. PROOF OF NAPIER'S RULES.

In his original treatise on this subject, Napier did in fact give a completely independent proof of these rules and this may be found in more advanced works.

However, for most practical purposes, it is sufficient proof to assume (or first prove) the cosine and/or four-part formula, and to show that Napier's Rules applied in turn to the parts of the triangle do in fact give the same set of equations.

For instance, we might proceed as follows.

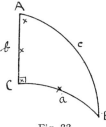

Fig. 33.

In the triangle ABC, right angled at C, we have, by the four-part formula:—

$$\cot a \sin b = \cot A \sin C + \cos b \cos C,$$

and if $C = 90°$, this becomes:—

$$\cot a \sin b = \cot A,$$

since $\sin 90° = 1$ and $\cos 90° = 0$

Let us now apply Napier's Rules to the three parts a, b, A (all three next to each other).

$$\sin b = \tan a \cot A$$

i.e. $\cot a \sin b = \cot A$, as already derived by the four-part formula.

A few more cases may be taken, and thus Napier's Rules may be demonstrated by shewing that they agree with results already obtained by fundamental formulae. This is normally all the proof that is required.

31. USE OF SIGNS IN A RIGHT ANGLED TRIANGLE.

Hitherto we have shown how to write down the appropriate equation connecting any three parts in a right angled triangle. We have not, however, considered the numerical values of these parts as given in a practical problem, and the effect those numerical values will have on the solution.

For instance, in the equation just given above, for a right angled triangle,

$$\cot A = \cot a \sin b \qquad \text{let } a = 116°$$
$$b = 32°$$

Then $\cot a$ is $-ve$, being an angle in the second quadrant, and $\sin b$ is $+ve$.

Hence $\cot A$ must be $-ve$, i.e. A must be in the second quadrant, that is, between 90° and 180°.

These facts have to be taken into account in a practical problem. There are different ways of doing this, and one is by the use of $+$ and $-$ signs as already illustrated.

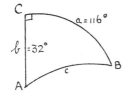

For instance, take triangle ABC, right angled at C. Find A.

By Napier's Rules,
$$\sin b = \tan a \cot A$$
$$\underset{-}{} \quad \underset{+}{} \quad \underset{-}{}$$
$$\cot A = \sin 32° \cot 116°$$

75° 30′ is not the answer, however. A must be greater than 90°, since its cotangent is $-ve$, so its correct value is 180° $-$ 75° 30′, i.e. $A = 104°$ 30′.	log cot log sin	9·68818 9·72421
	log cot A	9·41239
	giving	75° 30′

32. QUADRANTAL TRIANGLES, USE OF SIGNS.

Napier's Rules apply to quadrantal triangles with one important modification, which must be noted:—

In a quadrantal triangle, *if both adjacents or both opposites are both sides or both angles, put in a minus sign* (i.e. put a minus sign in front of the product).

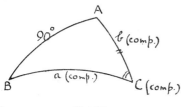

Fig, 34.

In the triangle ABC, let AB be the quadrant. Then A and B are next to the quadrant (i.e. the 90°), the other three parts are written down as complements. For example, given b and C, find A.

(b is the middle part, the other two are adjacents, and are both angles so "put in a minus sign").

By Napier's Rules,

$$\cos b = -\tan A \cot C$$

and $\tan A = -\cos b \tan C$

This means for instance, that if b and C are both less than 90°, then A is greater than 90°, since $\tan A$ is $-ve$.

Or again, find B.

$\sin B = \sin b \sin C$.   (No minus sign this time.)

IMPORTANT NOTE

To sum up the results of paragraphs 31 and 32:—

The sign of the resulting product of the two terms on one side must be the same, positive or negative, as the single term on the other side .... **N.B.**

33. The foregoing methods of employing signs are quite useful, and many readers will prefer them. In more theoretical cases, and particularly if the formulae are to be manipulated algebraically, the signs are more than useful—they are essential. They must be inserted and carried into the subsequent working, as we shall see later.

But in straight forward cases like the above, other readers will prefer to make use of the following simple rules, as given in para. 34.

34. PROPERTIES OF RIGHT ANGLED AND QUADRANTAL TRIANGLES.

(1) **In any right angled or quadrantal triangle, an angle and its opposite side are always of the same affection.**

("Of the same affection", i.e. both greater than 90°, or both less than 90°.)

This follows from formula (2) in para. 27, namely

$$\cot a \, \sin b = \cot A.$$

Since the sine is $+ve$ for all values up to 180°, it follows that cot a and cot A must be of the same sign, i.e. a and A must be of the same affection. Formula (3) similarly shows that b and B must be of the same affection.

So for instance, in the example just worked in para 31, since a is greater than 90°, we know at once that A must be, without having recourse to $+$ and $-$ signs at all.

This rule however tells us nothing about the side (or angle) opposite the right angle (or quadrant) so we need the following as well.

(2) **In any right angled triangle, we must have**
either, all three sides less than 90°
or, two sides greater and one less than 90°.

This follows from formula (1), para. 26, namely
$$\cos c = \cos a \, \cos b,$$
since cos c must have the same sign as the product cos a cos b. For this to happen we must have either all three cosines $+ve$ or only one $+ve$.

This rule applies equally in quadrantal triangles if we substitute angle for side and greater for less, i.e.
either **three angles greater than 90°**
or **two angles less and one greater**

These two rules will deal with every possible case. A few examples follow, using alternative methods of determining the correct solution.

35. **Example 1.**

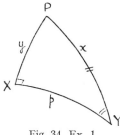

Fig. 34. Ex. 1

In the triangle PXY right angled at X, given $x = 118°$ 20′, $Y = 24°$ 05′, find p and y.

To find p.

Y is the middle part, x and p are adjacent, so,

$\cos Y = \tan p \cot x$

$\tan p = \cos Y \tan x$

(Our thoughts now run rather like this:—We already have x greater than 90°, y must be less because Y is, so p must be greater.)

log cos	9·96045
log tan	10·26825
log tan	10·22870
giving	59° 26′

$p = 120°\ 34'$.

To find y.

x and Y are together, y is on its own, so y is the middle part, x and Y are opposite, and

$$\sin y = \sin x \sin Y$$

log sin	9·94458
log sin	9·61073
log sin	9·55531
giving	21° 03′

(y must be of the same affection as Y)

$y = 21°\ 03'$.

Example 2.

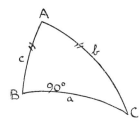

In the quadrantal triangle ABC in which $a = 90°$, given $b = 78°\ 14'$, $c = 49°\ 08'$, find A and B.

To find A.

A is the middle part, b and c are adjacent, so,

$\cos A = -\cot b \cot c$ (*Since both adjacents are both sides, we have put in a minus sign.*)

log cot	9·31870
log cot	9·93712
log cos	9·25582
giving	79° 37′

But $\cos A$ is $-ve$, and so,

$A = 100°\ 23'$

To find B.

B and c are together, b is on its own, so b is the middle part, the other two are opposite, and

$$\cos b = \sin c \cos B$$

$$\cos B = \cos b \ \operatorname{cosec} c$$

(B must be same affection as b)

$B = 74°\ 21'$.

log cos	9·30947
log cosec	10·12134
log cos	9·43081
giving	74° 21′

EXERCISE 2.

Solve the following right angled and quadrantal triangles, finding all the missing parts.

1. Triangle ABC, $a=94°\ 57'$ $B=60°\ 33'$, $A=90°$.

2. Triangle PAB, $A=111°\ 58'$ $B=101°\ 31'$, $P=90°$

3. Triangle XYZ, $X=73°\ 01'$, $y=47°\ 47'$, $x=90°$

4. Triangle ABC, $A=100°\ 50'$, $B=73°\ 10'$ $a=90°$

5. Triangle PXY, $p=53°\ 20'$, $X=92°\ 05'$, $Y=90°$

The questions which follow require some knowledge of the terrestrial sphere. The reader may care to look at paragraph 38 before proceeding.

6. The Great Circle distance between two positions A and B is 2100 n. mls. Given that A is on the Equator where the G.C. course is 037°, calculate the G.C. course at B and the difference of longitude between A and B.

7. A ship leaves lat. 35° 40′ N., long. 141° 00′ E. and follows a G.C. track. If the initial course is 060° 30′, find the latitude of the vertex.

8. A G.C. track westward from 49° 07′ S., 75° 50′ W. has its vertex in lat. 55° 00′ S. Calculate the initial course and the distance to the vertex.

9. From a ship A in south latitude a W/T station B is found to bear 084° T., distant 5400 n. mls. If B is in lat. 5° 10′ N., find the latitude of A.

10. The G.C. distance between A and B on the same parallel of latitude is 1000 n. mls, and the latitude of the vertex of the G.C. through A and B is 41° S. Calculate the latitude of A and B.

11. Calculate:
    (a) The G.C. distance from A in 25° 07′ S., 130° 20′ W. to B in 25° 07′ S., 152° 54′ E.
    (b) The latitude of the vertex.

12. From a W/T station B in long. 90° W. another station A on the Greenwich meridian bears 060° 33′ distant 5697 n. mls. Calculate the latitude of each station.

D

CHAPTER IV

AREA OF A SPHERICAL TRIANGLE. PROBLEMS.

36. AREA OF A LUNE.

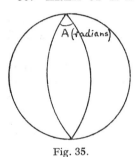

Fig. 35.

From first principles, it is clear that the area of a lune is the same fraction of the area of the sphere as the angle of the lune is of four right angles. If for instance, the angle of the lune is 60°, it is clear that

$$\text{Area of lune} = \text{Area of sphere} \times \frac{60}{360}$$

Or again, if the angle of the lune is A radians, and radius of sphere r then clearly

$$\frac{\text{Area of lune}}{\text{Area of sphere}} = \frac{A\,(\text{radians})}{2\pi\,(\text{radians})}$$

$$\textbf{Area of lune} = \frac{4\pi r^2 . A}{2\pi} = 2Ar^2 \qquad .. \quad \textbf{(1)}$$

37. AREA OF A SPHERICAL TRIANGLE ABC

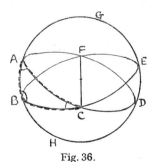

Fig. 36.

The figure illustrates triangle ABC on a sphere of radius r.

From symmetry, it is clear that triangle $CDE = FAB$ in area, i.e. area of lune $CBFAC =$ area $\triangle ABC + \triangle CDE$

34

Now, if A, B, C are the values of the angles in radians,

$$\triangle ABC + \text{area } BHDCB = \text{lune } AHDA = 2Ar^2$$
$$\triangle ABC + \text{area } AGECA = \text{lune } BGEB = 2Br^2$$
$$\triangle ABC + \triangle CDE = \text{lune } CBFAC = 2Cr^2, \text{ and adding,}$$
$$2\triangle ABC + 2\pi r^2 \text{ (hemisphere)} = 2(Ar^2 + Br^2 + Cr^2)$$
$$\therefore \text{ Area } \triangle ABC = r^2(A + B + C - \pi)$$

Now, $(A + B + C - \pi)$ is called the **Spherical excess**, E.

Thus, **area $\triangle ABC = Er^2$** ..   ..   ..   **(2)**

This form is sometimes useful. It does, however, require E to be in radians. It may be carried a step further, since

$$\frac{\triangle ABC}{2\pi r^2} = \frac{Er^2}{2\pi r^2} = \frac{E}{2\pi} \text{ (where } E \text{ is in radians)}$$

So, in words:—

The area of a spherical triangle is the same fraction of the area of a hemisphere as the spherical excess is of four right angles .... .N.B.

From this verbal statement, we may write

$$\mathbf{\frac{Area \ \triangle ABC}{Area \ hemisphere}} = \frac{E°}{360°} \quad .. \quad .. \quad \mathbf{(3)}$$

where $E° = (A° + B° + C° - 180°)$

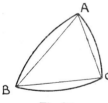
Fig. 37.

Finally then, by definition:—

The spherical excess is the amount by which the sum of the three angles of a spherical triangle ABC exceeds the sum of the three angles of the plane triangle ABC.

Example 1.

A spherical triangle has a spherical excess E of 1 second of arc. Find the area of the triangle if it is on the earth's surface, taking the radius of the earth to be 3960 statute miles.

$$\frac{\text{Area } \triangle}{\text{Area hemisphere}} = \frac{E}{360°} = \frac{1}{360 \times 60 \times 60}$$

i.e. Area $\triangle = \dfrac{2\pi \times (3960)^2}{360 \times 3600}$ which reduces to $\underline{76\cdot06 \text{ sq. mls.}}$

Example 2.

Find the angles and sides of an equilateral spherical triangle whose area is one fifth that of the sphere upon which it is described.

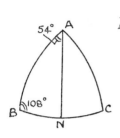

$$\frac{\text{Area} \triangle}{\text{Area sphere}} = \frac{1}{5} = \frac{E}{720°} \quad \text{whence}$$

$$E = \frac{720}{5} = \quad \begin{array}{r} 144° \\ 180° \\ \hline 3)324° \\ \hline 108° = \text{each angle.} \end{array}$$

Drop perp. AN, and by Napier's Rules	9·86126
$\cos AB = \cot 54 \cot 108$	9·51178
	9·37304
Each side $=103°\ 39'$.	76° 21'

38. THE TERRESTRIAL SPHERE.

The reader is assumed to be already familiar with the terms and definitions commonly employed in navigation and nautical astronomy.

Nevertheless, before proceeding to the solution of more difficult problems, we propose to give a brief summary of the principal terms used, without, however, attempting to define them in any way precisely. We shall deal only with those applications to navigation which assume the earth to be a perfect sphere.

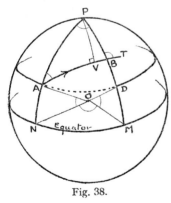

Referring to Fig. 38, in which A and B are two places on the earth's surface, P the pole of the earth, O the earth's centre.

Arc AN (or $\angle AON$) = latitude of A.

Arc BM (or $\angle BOM$) = latitude of B.

PA = co-lat. of A (i.e. complement of the latitude.)

PB = co-lat. of B.

AB = great circle track from A to B.

Fig. 38.

Length of arc AB (i.e. $\angle AOB$)=great circle distance from A to B.

PN, PM=meridians of A and B respectively.

Arc NM (or $\angle APB$)=difference of longitude (d. long.) between A and B.

Also, for a vessel on track from A towards B,
$\angle PAB$=initial course (or track angle)
$\angle PBT$=final course (,, ,, ,,)

V is the vertex of the great circle, i.e. the point at which the great circle is nearest to the Pole, so that PV is at right angles to the great circle AB.

Also AD is the distance along a parallel of latitude between the two meridians and when expressed in nautical miles, is called the *departure*.

39. To find the relation between departure and d. long. in any given latitude. (*Earth assumed a perfect sphere*).

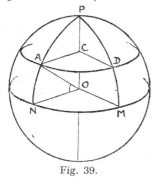

i.e. to compare the distance along a parallel, AD, between two meridians, with the corresponding distance, NM, along the equator.

The latitude of A is $\angle NOA$, and other parts of the figure have the usual meaning, as just discussed in para. 38.

Fig. 39.

Considering now the two planes CAD, ONM, they are parallel and equiangular. Hence, their corresponding sides are proportional, that is

$$\frac{AD}{NM} = \frac{CA}{ON} \qquad \text{....} \quad \text{....} \quad \text{....} \quad \text{....} \quad \text{....} \quad \text{....} \quad (1)$$

But $CA=OA$ cos latitude$=ON$ cos latitude and substituting in (1)

$$\frac{AD}{NM} = \frac{\text{dep.}}{\text{d. long.}} = \text{cos latitude} \quad \text{....} \qquad \text{....} \quad \text{....} \quad \text{....} \quad \text{N.B.}$$

Since a minute of arc at the equator is the same as a nautical mile, we may write

Departure (in n. mls) = d. long. (in minutes of arc) × cos latitude.

40. PROBLEMS ON THE TERRESTRIAL SPHERE.

The problems which follow in this chapter are typical of those set in the Specialist Navigators' Examinations at pass degree or equivalent standard. Although a fairly complete break-dcwn of the problems is given, we have decided not to burden the reader with the tedious repetition of logarithmic computations. In order to get maximum benefit from these examples, therefore, *it is suggested that they should be worked out in full by the student.*

Example 3.

A vessel steers westwards on a great circle from 25° N., 120° W. to 58° N. If the d. long. is equal to the great circle distance, find the longitude of arrival and the final course.

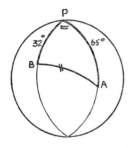

In the $\triangle PAB$, by hav formula,
hav $AB =$ hav P sin PA sin $PB+$
hav $(PA \sim PB)$
and since $AB = P$, we have
hav $P =$ hav P sin 65° sin 32°+hav 33°

and hav $P = \dfrac{\text{hav } 33°}{1 - \sin 65° \sin 32°}$

Solving this by logs gives $P = 46°$ 24′ and longitude of arrival $= 166°$ 24′ W.

By sine formula, $\dfrac{\sin B}{\sin 65°} = \dfrac{\sin P}{\sin AB} = 1$

i.e. sin $B =$ sin 65°, $B = 65°$ and

final course $= N$ 65° W. or 295° T.

Example 4.

On a given great circle from A to B the initial track angle was 042° 16′ and the final track angle 116° 44′, the distance being 2356 n.m. If A is in long. 02° 16′ E., find the lat. and long. of B.

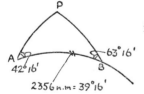

Here we have two angles and the side included, so in the polar triangle,
$a' = 137°$ 44′
$b' = 116°$ 44′
$P' = 140°$ 44′   and

hav p' =hav P' sin a' sin b'+hav $(a' \sim b')$ from which
$p' = 97°$ 36′
and so $P = 82°$ 24′
and long. of $B = 84°$ 40′ E.

$$\text{Hav } A' = \frac{\text{hav } a' - \text{hav } (b' \sim p')}{\sin b' \sin p'} \quad \text{from which}$$

$$A' = 154° \ 34'$$
$$\text{and } a = 25° \ 26'$$

whence lat. of $B = \underline{64° \ 34' \text{ N.}}$

Example 5.

An aircraft flies along a great circle from A in lat. 49° 30′ N. for a distance of 1440 n.m., to B. At A the course is N. $\theta°$ E. and at B it is N. 2 $\theta°$ E. Find the initial course and the latitude of B.

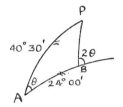

By four-part formula,
cot PA sin $AB =$ cot $(180° - 2 \ \theta)$ sin $\theta +$ cos θ cos AB
and putting cot PA sin $AB = Q$ (which can be evaluated later) we have

$$Q = -\cot 2 \ \theta \sin \theta + \cos \theta \cos 24° \quad .... \quad .... \quad \text{using } A.3$$

$$= \cos \theta \cos 24° - \sin \theta \cdot \frac{\cos^2 \theta - \sin^2 \theta}{2 \sin \theta \cos \theta} \quad .... \quad \text{using } A.7$$

i.e. $\quad \dfrac{2 \cos^2 \theta \cos 24° - \cos^2 \theta + 1 - \cos^2 \theta}{2 \cos \theta} = Q$

$\cos^2 \theta \ (2 \cos 24° - 2) + 1 = 2Q \cos \theta$ which reduces to
$\cdot 173 \cos^2 \theta + \cdot 952 \cos \theta - 1 = 0$ and solution of this equation gives $\theta = 25° \ 36'$
i.e. Initial course $= \underline{\text{N. } 25° \ 36' \text{ E.}}$

By sine formula.

$$\frac{\sin PB}{\sin 25° \ 36'} = \frac{\sin 40° \ 30'}{\sin 128° \ 48'} \quad \text{whence}$$

$$PB = 111° \ 06' \text{ and lat } B = 68° \ 54'.$$

Example 6.

A ship is on a G.C. track from A in lat 47° 25′ S., long 06° 10′ E., to B in lat 18° 30′ S., long. 63° 16′ E. Find the latitude of the ship at the point C on the G.C. when she has altered her longitude by an amount equal to half the d. long. between the two places.

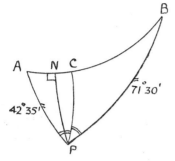

Let C be the point in question, so that $\angle APC = \angle BPC = 28° 33'$. Drop perp. PN.

In $\triangle PAB$ (two sides and included angle) hav $AB =$ hav $P\sin PA \sin PB +$ hav $(PA \sim PB)$
whence $AB = 54° 21'$

and again, hav $B = \dfrac{\text{hav } PA - \text{hav } (PB \sim AB)}{\sin PB \sin AB}$ whence

$\angle B = 44° 19'\cdot 7$
In $\triangle PNB$, by Napier's Rules,
$\qquad \sin PN = \sin B \sin PB$ and $PN = 41° 30'\cdot 5$
$\qquad \cos PB = \cot \angle BPN \cot B$
$\qquad\qquad\qquad$ and $\angle BPN = 72° 47'$.
So $\angle CPN = 44° 14'$
$\qquad$ In $\triangle CPN$, $\cos \angle CPN = \tan PN \cot PC$ whence
$\qquad PC = 51° 00'\cdot 5$ and lat. of $C = 38° 59'\cdot 5$ S.

41. The Celestial Sphere.

To an observer on the earth and looking out into space, the earth may be imagined as if surrounded by a vast sphere on whose surface all the heavenly bodies appear to move. This imaginary sphere is called the **celestial sphere** (or sometimes the celestial concave.)

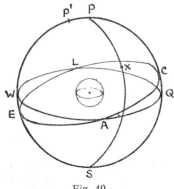

Referring to Fig. 40, which depicts the celestial sphere surrounding the earth :—

P and $S =$ the celestial poles.
$WQ =$ celestial equator (sometimes called the equinoctial).
$EC =$ the ecliptic, i.e. the apparent path of the true sun during the year. The true sun is always on the ecliptic.
$P' =$ the pole of the ecliptic.

Fig. 40.

$A =$ First Point of Aries, the point in which the sun crosses from South to North declination.

$L =$ First Point of Libra, the point in which the sun crosses from North to South declination.

$\angle CAQ =$ Obliquity of the ecliptic, which may be taken as $23° \ 28'$ in a practical problem.

Thus, arcs QC, WE, PP' are all equal to $23° \ 28'$.

$PXS =$ celestial meridian, which corresponds exactly to a terrestrial meridian.

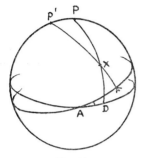

Again, considering the body X on the celestial sphere, in Fig. 41.

Fig. 41.

$AD =$ Right Ascension of X, that is, the arc of the equinoctial measured Eastwards from the First Point of Aries to the meridian through X.

$XD =$ Declination of X. This corresponds to latitude on the earth.

$PX =$ Polar Distance (the complement of the declination).

$AF =$ celestial longitude, that is, the arc of the ecliptic measured Eastwards from the First Point of Aries, to the point in which the great circle from P' through X meets the ecliptic.

$XF =$ celestial latitude, that is, angular distance north or south of the ecliptic. (It will be noted that celestial latitude and celestial longitude are quite different from latitude and longitude on the earth.)

42. PROBLEMS ON THE CELESTIAL SPHERE.

Here again, outline solutions only are given and the student should work through these problems in full.

Example 7.

Calculate the celestial latitude and longitude of a star whose declination is $26° \ 16'·7$ S. and R.A. 16h 25m 05s. Take the obliquity of the ecliptic to be $23° \ 28'$.

R.A. 16h 25m 05s $= 246° \ 16'·25$

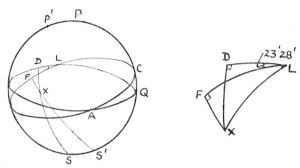

In dealing with this problem, we are a little hampered by the fact that the figure is rather awkward to draw. The enlarged diagram will help.

$AQLD$ is the R.A., thus $LD=66°\ 16'\cdot25$
and decl. (south)$=XD=26°\ 16'\cdot7$
Obliquity of the ecliptic$=\angle DLF=23°\ 28'$
$\qquad$ Join XL
By Napier's Rules: In $\triangle DLX$
$\sin LD=\tan XD \cot \angle DLX$ whence $\angle DLX=28°\ 20'\cdot3$
Again $\cos LX=\cos LD \cos XD$ whence $LX=68°\ 51'\cdot0$
In $\triangle LFX$, $\angle FLX=28°\ 20'\cdot3-23°\ 28'=4°\ 52'\cdot3$
and by Napier's Rules
$\sin FX=\sin LX \sin \angle FLX$ whence $FX=4°\ 33'\cdot0$
i.e. cel. lat.$=\underline{4°\ 33'\cdot0\ S.}$

Again, in $\triangle LFX$,
$\cos \angle FLX=\tan FL \cot LX$ whence $FL=68°\ 46'\cdot7$
i.e. cel. long.$=\underline{248°\ 46'\cdot7.}$

Example 8.

Two stars X and Y have the same R.A., 04h 12m 04s., the declination of X being 58° 00′ N. and of Y, 18° 00′ N. A third star Z bears N. 76° W. from X and N. 66° W. from Y. Find the R.A. of Z.

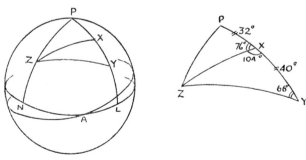

The figure illustrates the data given. X and Y are the two stars on the same meridian, PL, since they have the same R.A., arc AL. Z is as shown, and either $\angle P$ or arc LAN is the difference between its R.A. and the R.A. of X and Y.

In $\triangle ZXY$, find ZX by four-part formula.

cot ZX sin 40°=cot 66° sin 104°+cos 40° cos 104°

cot ZX=cot 66° sin 104° cosec 40°+cot 40° cos 104°

from which ZX=69° 00′

In $\triangle ZXP$, find $\angle P$ by four-part formula.

cot 69° sin 32°=cot P sin 76°+cos 32° cos 76°

from which $\angle P$=90° 06′=6h 00m 24s

Hence, R.A. of Z=22h 11m 40s.

43. THE CELESTIAL OR RATIONAL HORIZON.

The observers zenith, Z, is the point in which a line from the earth's centre passing through the observer's position would cut the celestial sphere.   In simpler (though perhaps not so precise) terms, it is the point vertically above the observer's head.

The celestial or rational horizon is the great circle on the celestial sphere, every point of which is 90° from the zenith.   Thus, the rational horizon divides the celestial sphere into two hemispheres. The upper one, with Z, the zenith, at its centre, contains all the heavenly bodies which are above the horizon and so are visible to the observer.

It is sometimes convenient to use the diagram obtained by projecting the celestial concave on to the plane of the rational horizon.

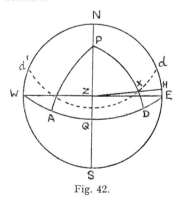

Fig. 42.

Thus, the circle represents the rational horizon, and Z the zenith is at its centre.

Vertical circles are those great circles which pass through the observer's zenith and therefore meet the horizon at right angles.

NZS=observer's meridian.

WZE=prime vertical, that is the vertical circle passing through the east and west points of the horizon.

Since ZS (from zenith to horizon) represents 90° of arc, an observer in say 30° N. latitude would be as shown at Z, where ZQ is one third of ZS.

WQE=celestial equator or equinoctial

ZQ=latitude and PZ=co-lat.

P=Pole, and of course PQ=90°

and NP, the elevation of the pole above the horizon, is
equal to ZQ the latitude.

If X is a heavenly body then

XD=declination of body.

The small circle dXd' is sometimes referred to as the "parallel of declination", a useful conception in that it gives an indication of the path of the body across the celestial concave. The term should be used with reservations, however, since the declination is not necessarily constant throughout the day and so dXd' is not a "parallel". In any event, it is not a great circle and cannot be used as part of any triangle.

To return to the figure;—

PX=polar distance of body.

XH=true altitude of body.

ZX=zenith distance of body.

$\angle ZPX$=local hour angle (East). More precisely L.H.A. should be expressed Westwards from the meridian, from 0°—360°. Thus, L.H.A. 300° is correct, but for convenience in a problem, we sometimes call this "an hour angle of 60° East".

Again, an "hour angle of 6 hrs" (East or West) would mean that the meridian through the body passed through E. or W., i.e. the angle at the Pole between the meridian through the body and the observer's meridian is a right angle.

$\angle PZX$=bearing or azimuth of the body. Note that *bearing* can be expressed as we choose, e.g. N. 70° E., 070°: or S. 20° W., 200° T., and so on. *Azimuth* should only be expressed from 0°—180°, measured east or west from the elevated pole, e.g. N. 110° E., N. 165° W. etc., for an observer in the Northern Hemisphere. Failure to appreciate this can lead to trouble in problems.

A=First Point of Aries. Like all other points on the celestial concave, this appears to rotate from East to West across the sky.

Hence, to an observer at Z, $\angle ZPA$ is the L.H.A. of the First Point of Aries.

Arc AD, as we have seen, is the R.A. of the body X.

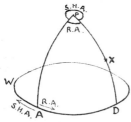

The Sidereal Hour Angle of the body is defined as the arc of the equinoctial measured westwards, from the First Point of Aries to the meridian through the body, i.e.
arc AWD=S.H.A. of X.
arc AD=R.A. of X.

Fig. 43.

Clearly, these may equally well be defined as the angles at the Pole, as shown, since arc $AD=\angle APD$ and so on.

The worked examples which follow will show the use of this figure in solving problems. *It is suggested that they should be worked out in full.*

44. Problems on the plane of the rational horizon.

Example 9.

In lat. 30° N. a star is observed bearing 270° T. and after hanging its hour angle by 11° 15′ it set. Find its declination.

Let 11° 15′=α for easier working.

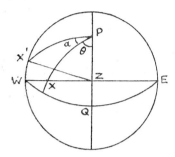

The circle represents the rational horizon, Z the observer, P the pole, PZ the co-lat.=60°.

X and X' the two positions of the star, and $PX=PX'$, the polar distance.

In $\triangle PXZ$, by Napier's Rules, ($\angle PZX=90°$)
$$\cos \theta=\tan PZ \cot PX \quad .... \qquad .... \qquad .... \qquad .... \qquad .... \qquad (1)$$

In quadrantal $\triangle PZX'$, ($ZX'=90°$)
$$\cos (\theta+\alpha) =-\cot PZ \cot PX .... \qquad .... \qquad .... \qquad .... \qquad (2)$$

Note insertion of minus sign: see important note in paragraph 32. For instance, in (1) above, PZ is less than 90°, its tangent is positive. So is cot PX. θ is less than 90°, its cosine is positive, i.e. positive=positive.

In (2), cot PZ and cot PX are both positive. $(\theta+\alpha)$ however, is more than 90° and its cosine is therefore negative. Hence, insert minus sign. We now have negative=negative.

To return to the problem, it is now just a question of solving equations (1) and (2).

Since cot PX is common to each, we easily obtain

$\cos \theta \cot PZ=-\tan PZ \cos (\theta+\alpha)$

$\cos \theta \cot PZ=-\tan PZ (\cos \theta \cos \alpha-\sin \theta \sin \alpha)$ using A. 5.

$\cot PZ \qquad =-\tan PZ (\cos \alpha-\tan \theta \sin \alpha)$

$\cot^2 PZ \qquad =\tan \theta \sin \alpha-\cos \alpha$

$\tan \theta \qquad =\dfrac{\cot^2 PZ+\cos \alpha}{\sin \alpha}$ and solving this

by logs gives $\theta=81° 33′·5$

In (1) cot $PX=\cos \theta \cos PZ$ whence

$PX=85° 09′$ and so Declination $=4° 51′$ N.

Example 10.

An observer in N. latitude notes that when star *Capella*, (Decl. 45° 57' N., S.H.A. 281° 36') is rising another star, *Kaus Australis* (Decl. 34° 24' S., S.H.A. 084° 38') bears exactly 180° from the bearing of *Capella*. Find the latitude of the observer.

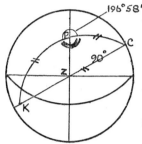

The figure is on the plane of the rational horizon, $C = Capella$, on the horizon, $K = Kaus\ Australis$.

PZ = observer's co-lat.

The difference between the S.H.A.'s is 196° 58', which is therefore the angle at the pole between their meridians.

Hence, the angle $\angle KPC$ in the $\triangle KPC$ is 360° − 196° 58', i.e. 163° 02'.

In the $\triangle KPC$,

$\angle KPC = 163° 02'$

$PC \quad = 44° 03'$ (polar distance of C)

$PK \quad = 124° 24'$ (polar distance of K)

$\sim \quad = 80° 21'$ and,

hav KC = hav P sin PC sin PK + hav $(PC \sim PK)$ .... (1)

from which $KC = 162° 39'$

In quadrantal $\triangle PZC$, by Napier's Rules

cos PZ = sin PC cos $\angle C$ .... (2)

To find $\angle C$ we have, in $\triangle PCK$,

$$\frac{\sin \angle C}{\sin PK} = \frac{\sin \angle KPC}{\sin KC} \quad .... \quad .... \quad .... \quad .... \quad .... \quad (3)$$

sin $\angle C$ = sin 124° 24' sin 163° 02' cosec 162° 39'

from which $\angle C = 53° 50' \cdot 5$

And in (2) cos PZ = sin 44° 03' cos 53° 50'·5

whence latitude of observer = 65° 47' N.

Example 11.

At a certain place in the Southern hemisphere, when the sun's declination was θ, the length of the day was 15h 20m. When the declination was $\dfrac{\theta}{2}$ the length of the day was 13h 36m. Find the latitude of the place and the declination on the shorter day.

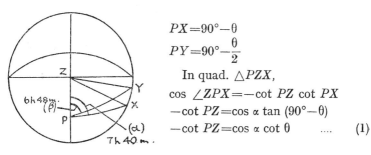

$PX = 90° - \theta$

$PY = 90° - \dfrac{\theta}{2}$

In quad. $\triangle PZX$,

$\cos \angle ZPX = -\cot PZ \cot PX$

$-\cot PZ = \cos \alpha \tan (90° - \theta)$

$-\cot PZ = \cos \alpha \cot \theta$ .... (1)

In quad. $\triangle PZY$, $\cos \angle ZPY = -\cot PZ \cot PY$

$$-\cot PZ = \cos \beta \cot \dfrac{\theta}{2} \qquad .... \qquad .... \qquad .... \qquad (2)$$

From (1) and (2), equating, we get

$$\tan \theta \cos \beta = \tan \dfrac{\theta}{2} \cos \alpha \qquad \text{and putting } \tan \dfrac{\theta}{2} = t,$$

we have $\dfrac{2t}{1-t^2} \cdot \dfrac{1}{t} = \dfrac{\cos \alpha}{\cos \beta} = 2 \cdot 0327$ .... using A. 7

and $t^2 = \dfrac{\cdot 0327}{2 \cdot 0327}$ whence $\dfrac{\theta}{2} = 7° 13' \cdot 5 =$ Declination on shorter day.

From (2) we get latitude $= 58° 37' \cdot 5$ S.

Example 12.

Exactly 1h 30m after rising the hour angle of the sun was 6 hrs. and its altitude 15°. Find the latitude of the place and the declination of the sun. (Assume northern hemisphere).

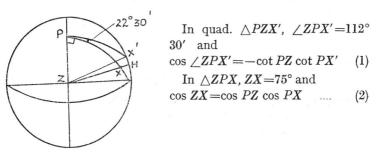

In quad. $\triangle PZX'$, $\angle ZPX' = 112°$ 30' and

$\cos \angle ZPX' = -\cot PZ \cot PX'$ (1)

In $\triangle ZPX$, $ZX = 75°$ and

$\cos ZX = \cos PZ \cos PX$ .... (2)

$(2) \div (1)$ gives $\dfrac{\cos ZX}{\cos \angle ZPX'} = -\sin PZ \sin PX$

$\cdot 6763 = \sin PZ \sin PX$ .... (3)

(2)+(3)   cos $(PZ\sim PX)$ =cos ZX+ ·6763 = ·9352

(2)−(3)   cos $(PZ+PX)$ =cos ZX− ·6763 = − ·4176

(using A. 5)

Whence $PZ\sim PX$ =20° 44′

$\qquad PZ+PX$ =114° 41′

and by adding and subtracting, $PX \quad$ =67° 42′·5

$\qquad\qquad\qquad\qquad\qquad$ Decl. =22° 17′·5 N.

$\qquad\qquad\qquad\qquad\qquad$ Lat. =43° 01′·5 N.

Example 13.

The sun rises at the same instant when observed from A, in lat. 57° 08′ N., long. 2° 04′ W. as from B, in lat. 13° 00′ S., long. 38° 30′ W. Calculate its declination.

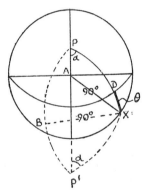

This is an awkward combination of two sets of data in one diagram.

Let XD=decl.=0

Let HA on rising be α, at A.

Then it will be (α+36° 26′) at B.

$\qquad PX$ =90+θ

$\qquad P'X$ =90−θ

In quad. $\triangle APX$,

$\qquad$ cos α=−cot PA cot (90+θ)$\qquad\qquad$ and using A. 3

$\qquad$ cos α=cot PA tan θ ....$\qquad$ .... $\qquad$ .... $\qquad$ .... $\qquad$ .... $\qquad$ (1)

In quad. $\triangle BP'X$,

$\qquad$ cos (α+36° 26′)=−cot $P'B$ tan θ .... $\qquad$ .... $\qquad$ .... $\qquad$ (2)

Solving (1) and (2) gives α=58° 05′ from which

$\qquad$ θ=18° 52′=Declination.

Example 14.

Two observers on the same meridian observe the altitude of a star at the same instant. At A the altitude is 41° 09′ and at B it is

30° 59'. B is in lat. 20° S. Find the latitude of A if the azimuth of the star is θ at B and 2 θ at A.

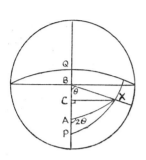

Since azimuth is measured from the elevated pole, A must be to the southward of B, as shown

$$BX = 59°\ 01',\ AX = 48°\ 51',\ BQ = 20°$$

In $\triangle ABX$, by sine formula,

$$\frac{\sin (180 - 2\theta)}{\sin BX} = \frac{\sin \theta}{\sin AX} \qquad \dots \qquad (1)$$

from which $\theta = 55°\ 18'$.

Drop perp. XC, and by Napier's rules, find BC ($= 43°\ 28'·4$) and AC ($= 21°$ $55'·8$)

Lat $A = BQ + BC + AC =$
$$85°\ 24'·2\ S.$$

EXERCISE 3.

PROBLEMS IN SPHERICAL TRIGONOMETRY

These may all be solved by methods previously dealt with, that is, haversine formula (with polar triangle). sine formula (if no ambiguity). four-part formula (occasionally), together with the ability to drop a perpendicular and use Napier's Rules either in right angled or quadrantal triangles.

1. The area of an isosceles right angled triangle is $\frac{1}{6}$ that of the hemisphere on which it is drawn. Find the side opposite the right angle.

2. Find the angles in the equilateral triangle ABC whose area is $\frac{1}{10}$ that of the hemisphere.

   If D is the mid-point of BC, show by calculation that
2. $AD + BC = \pi R$, where R is the radius of the sphere.

3. Find the area in sq. inches of a spherical triangle ABC in which $A = 26°\ 42'$, $B = 48°\ 15'$, $C = 112°\ 27'$, drawn on a reduced earth of radius 40 inches.

4. A right angled spherical isosceles triangle has an area equal to $\frac{1}{9}$ of the sphere on which it is drawn. Find the side opposite the right angle.

5. The area of a spherical triangle is 140 sq. in. and the radius of the sphere upon which it is drawn is 35 in. If the angles of the triangle are in the ratio $1 ; 2 ; 5$, find each angle in degrees correct in two decimal places.

6. Use the formula, area of triangle $= ER^2$ to find the area of a triangle PZX in which $P = 62°$, $Z = 126°$ and $p = 90°$, the radius of the sphere, R, being 24 inches.

E

7. The d. long. between two places A and B in the Northern hemisphere is 71° 51'·5. The G.C. bearing of B from A is 057° 26' 45'' and of A from B is 265° 59' 15''. What are the latitudes of A and B?

8. An observer is in lat. 21° 30' N. and longitude east (unknown). He obtains a great circle bearing from X, in 56° 15' N., 10° 00' W. and observes that the same great circle passes through Y, in 42° 50' N., 9° 12' E. Find the observer's longitude.

9. The R.A. of the true sun is 04h 10m 20s and the obliquity of the ecliptic is 23° 28'. Find the sun's declination, celestial latitude and longitude.

10. On a great circle track commencing from 75° 40' W. in the northern hemisphere the distance is 3,630 miles, the initial course being 056° T. and final course 112° T. Find the position arrived at.

11. A star is in celestial lat. 04° 14'·8 N., long. 048° 37'·5. Find its R.A. and declination.

12. The sun's declination is 20° 02' N. Find its true altitude when bearing 270° T. to an observer in lat. 43° 09' N.

13. The sun's declination is 23° 27' N. Find its hour angle and altitude when on the prime vertical bearing 090° T., to an observer in lat. 50° 47' N.

14. The R.A. of a heavenly body is 16h 14m 04s and its declination is 25° 51' N. Find its celestial latitude and longitude.

15. Two stars bear due West at the same instant, the observer being in lat. 50° 47' S. Their altitudes are 19° 58' and 40° 01'. Find the difference between their hour angles.

16. When a heavenly body has a L.H.A. 270°, its altitude is 18° 44' and declination 21° 55' N. Find the observer's latitude.

17. An observer is in lat. 50° 45' N. and the moon's declination is 23° 42' N. when its L.H.A. is 090°. Find its altitude and azimuth.

18. The sun is observed to rise bearing S. 80° E. to an observer in lat. 49° 49' N. Find its L.H.A.

19. The altitude of a star when due West was 20° 02' and it set bearing 281° 15'. Find the latitude of the observer.

20. The angles of a spherical triangle on a sphere of radius R are 116°, 46°, 36°. Find the side of an equilateral triangle of area equal to that of the first, but described on a sphere of radius $2R$.

21. Calculate the latitude in which the stars Canopus and Spica will be at their maximum azimuths simultaneously using:—
    Canopus;   Decl. 52° 40′·0 S., R.A. 06h 23m 08s.
    Spica;   Decl. 10° 58′·0 S., R.A. 13h 23m 16s.

22. The declination of a body is 38° 18′·5 N. and its R.A. is 01h 26m 11s. Calculate its celestial latitude and longitude.

23. When its L.H.A. was 090° the altitude of the sun was 15° 02′ and 1h 29m later it set. Calculate the latitude of the observer and the declination of the sun.

24. The altitude of a star when due South was 39° 28′ and when due West was 10° 06′. Find the latitude of the observer.

25. The sun's meridian altitude was 55° 51′ and its hour angle on setting was 105° 12′. Calculate the latitude of the place.

26. Find the latitude of a place where the stars Castor and Alphard will be observed to rise at the same instant using:—
    Castor;   Decl. 31° 58′ N., S.H.A. 246° 56′
    Alphard;   Decl. 8° 30′ S., S.H.A. 218° 33′

27. The bearing of the sun on rising is observed to be N. 60° E. and at 6.00 a.m. L.A.T. the bearing is N. 76° E. Calculate the observer's latitude and the sun's declination.

28. The sun's altitude when bearing due West was 28° 12′ and at 6.00 p.m. L.A.T. was 15° 08′. Find the latitude of the place.

29. At noon on the shortest day the shadow cast by a perpendicular rod was eight times as long as the shadow at noon on the longest day. Find the latitude, the declination on the longest day being 23° 28′ S.

30. An observer is in lat. 20° 06′ N. and the sun's declination is 23° 20, N. Find its maximum azimuth and the time at which this occurs during the morning.

31. To a stationary observer, the length of the day when the sun's declination is 12° 15′ S., is three times the length of the day when the declination is 23° 28′ N. Find the latitude of the observer.

32. The sun rose with an hour angle of 113° 50′ E. and at 6.00 a.m. L.A.T. its altitude was 14° 44′. Find the sun's declination and the latitude of the observer.

33. At 1800 hrs. L.A.T. the sun's altitude was 15° 22′ and it set bearing N. 58° W. Find the latitude of the observer.

34. An aircraft is flying along the G.C. track from A in lat. 47° 24′ N., long. 6° 11′ W., to B in lat. 18° 28′ N., long. 63° 21′ W. Find its latitude when it has altered its longitude by an amount equal to half the d. long. between the two places.

35. From a star Z (Decl. 20° 00' N., S.H.A. 278° 16') a second star X lies at an angular distance of 28° 50' and on a bearing of 078° T. A third star Y is at an angular distance of 90° 00' from Z and 67° 16' from X. Find the S.H.A. of Y.

36. A vessel in lat. 32° 12' N., long. 68° 40' W. takes a radio bearing of 042·5° of an unknown transmitter who gave its latitude as 52° 33' N. but whose longitude was lost in atmospherics. Calculate the longitude of the transmitter.

37. If the sun is observed to set simultaneously in Belfast (54° 41' N., 5° 44' W.) and in Recife (08° 03' S., 34° 52' W.), calculate the sun's declination.

38. The sun's meridian altitude bearing South was 61° 46' and its altitude at 6.00 p.m. L.A.T. was 15° 42'. Calculate the observer's latitude and the sun's declination.

39. From a W/T station A in lat. 48° 42' N., long. 5° 06' W. the D/F bearing of a ship in distress was 244° T. and simultaneously, from a station B in lat. 40° 40' N., long. 2° 16' W. the bearing was 297° T. Find the distance of the ship from B.

40. Two places are in the same lat. 52° 14' N. and in longitudes respectively 12° 22' E. and 69° 40' E. If the distance in nautical miles between them along the parallel exceeds the G.C. distance by an amount given by

$$R[\theta \cos \text{lat} - 2 \sin^{-1} (\cos \text{lat} \sin \tfrac{\theta}{2})], \text{ where } \theta = d \text{ long}.$$

in radians, calculate a value for R, the radius of the earth, in nautical miles.

41. To a stationary observer, the sun set on the rational horizon with L.H.A. 103° 45', when the difference between its declination and the observer's latitude was 24° 16'. Calculate the latitude and declination.

42. Two positions, A and B are in the same south latitude. A third position, C, also in south latitude is 90° in longitude east of B, whilst the G.C. distance from C to A is 5,400 miles. From C, the G.C. bearing of A is 222° and of B is 252°. Find the latitudes of A, B and C.

43. At a place in south latitude the stars Sirius and Regulus were observed to set in the rational horizon at the same instant. Calculate the latitude of the observer.
    Sirius decl. 16° 39'·5 S., S.H.A. 259° 10'·0
    Regulus decl. 12° 10'·0 N., S.H.A. 208° 27'·0

44. Three stars A (decl. 13° S., S.H.A. 37°), B (decl. 29° S., S.H.A. 22°) and C (S.H.A. 244°) are observed on the rational

horizon at the same instant, A and B setting, C rising, the observer being in north latitude. Find C's declination.

45. Star Z has declination 21° 28′ N. and is on the G.C. passing through two other stars, X (decl. 42° 48′ N., R.A. 12h 55m) and Y (decl. 56° 12′ N., R.A. 14h 12m). Find the R.A. of Z, which is to the westward of X.

46. Two observers are on the same meridian 04° 12′ E. A in lat. 55° N., B in lat. 15° N. A D/F station bears 075° from A and 067° from B, both being G.C. bearings. Calculate the longitude of the D/F station.

47. To an observer in the southern hemisphere, a star bears 122° T. and after changing its hour angle by 42° 30′ it again bears 122° T., having in the meantime attained its position of maximum azimuth, bearing 118° T. Calculate the declination of the star and the observer's latitude.

48. An aircraft flies along a G.C. track in the northern hemisphere for a distance of 3600 miles, her initial and final track angles being 058° T. and 110° T. respectively. Find the d. long. made good.

49. An observer in north latitude notes star X (decl. 46° 02′ N. S.H.A. 101° 36′) rising, and at the same instant that the difference between the bearing of X and the bearing of another star Y (decl. 27° 01′ S., S.H.A. 256° 32′) is 180°. Find the observer's latitude.

50. From a vessel on the Equator a star is observed bearing 221° T. After steaming 090° T., 20 miles, the star bore 258° T., its G.H.A. having altered by 22° in the interval. Find the declination of the star.

51. A star whose declination is 19° 24′ N. changes its azimuth by 38° 10′ between crossing the prime vertical and setting. Find the latitude of the observer.

52. The area of a spherical triangle ABC is $\frac{1}{6}$ that of the sphere on which it is drawn. If angles A and C are 68° and 82° respectively calculate the length of side AC.

53. A star whose declination is 15° 55′ S. changes its hour angle by 60° 10′ between crossing the prime vertical and the observer's meridian. Calculate the observer's latitude.

54. A vessel steers easterly on a Great Circle from a position 58° S., 55° E. to a position in 25° S. Find the longitude of arrival, the final course and the distance steamed.

CHAPTER V.

SUPPLEMENTAL THEOREM. IDENTITIES. FORMULAE

45. Further application of the Supplemental Theorem.

Consider the fundamental cosine formula in any triangle ABC, namely,

$$\cos a = \cos b \cos c + \sin b \sin c \cos A \quad \dots \quad \dots \quad \dots \quad (1)$$

Since $a = 180° - A'$, $b = 180 - B'$ and so on, we can write

$$\cos (180° - A') = \cos (180° - B') \cos (180° - C') +$$
$$\sin (180° - B') \sin (180° - C') \cos (180° - a')$$

i.e. $-\cos A' = -\cos B' \cdot -\cos C' + \sin B' \sin C' \cdot -\cos a'$

(using A.3)

$$-\cos A' = \cos B' \cos C' - \sin B' \sin C' \cos a'$$

$$\cos a' = \frac{\cos B' \cos C' + \cos A'}{\sin B' \sin C'} \ . \text{ So we have derived}$$

a quite new formula, which applies whatever the values of B', C', etc., may be. In short, it is quite general and may simply be written

$$\cos a = \frac{\cos B \cos C + \cos A}{\sin B \sin C} \quad \dots \quad \dots \quad VIIIa.$$

a formula which applies to any triangle ABC.

Note that this formula gives a side in terms of the three angles. We shall not often use it to calculate a side, since the haversine formula is better for this purpose. In proving identities, however, it is particularly useful as it enables us to *get small letters into big letters*, providing of course, we have *cos a*, or *b*, or *c* to deal with.

With practice, intervening steps may be cut out. It will be observed that we simply replace small letters by big ones, or vice versa, and reverse the sign wherever a term contains a single cosine. For example,

$$\cos b = \cos c \cos a + \sin c \sin a \cos B, \text{ and so}$$
$$-\cos B = \cos C \cos A - \sin C \sin A \cos b \text{ and}$$

$$\cos b = \frac{\cos C \cos A + \cos B}{\sin C \sin A} \quad \dots \quad \dots \quad VIIIb.$$

Clearly, by the same method

$$\cos c = \frac{\cos A \cos B + \cos C}{\sin A \sin B} \quad \dots \quad \dots \quad VIIIc.$$

We shall return to these later.

46.   There are one or two practical applications of the supplemental theorem which are sometimes useful.

Note that $a>b$ means "a greater than b"

and $a<b$ means "a less than b"

We can deal with inequalities exactly as we deal with equations, except in one respect:—if we multiply through by -1 we must reverse the inequality sign.

Thus, if $a+b+d>c$

then $a+b>c-d$

and $2(a+b)>2(c-d)$ and so on.

But, if $a+b>c$.

then$-a-b<-c$.

The reader may easily verify the foregoing by taking one or two numerical examples.

(*a*)   Now take a fundamental property of any spherical triangle, and apply it to the polar triangle, namely that

$$a'+b'+c'>0$$

By the supplemental theorem,

$$(180°-A)+(180°-B)+(180°-C)>0$$
$$-A-B-C>-540°$$

i.e. $A+B+C<540°$,

a fact we had already deduced in para. 10, but which we have now established by a different method.

(*b*)   Or again, in radians, for example, in any spherical (polar) triangle we must have

$$A'+B'+C'>\pi$$
$$(\pi-a)+(\pi-b)+(\pi-c)>\pi$$
$$3\pi-a-b-c>\pi$$
$$a+b+c<2\pi,$$

again, a fact we had already established by other means (para. 10).

(*c*)   Yet again, take a fundamental property of any triangle namely, that the sum of any two sides must be greater than the third, e.g.

$$a'+b'>c' \qquad \text{and so}$$
$$(\pi-A)+(\pi-B)>\pi-C$$
$$A+B-C<\pi \quad \dots \quad \dots \quad \dots \quad \dots \quad \dots \quad (1)$$

whence $A-C<\pi-B$

This result may be expressed in general terms:—

The difference between any two angles of a spherical triangle is less than the supplement of the third angle .... N.B.

Although illustrated above for A, B and C in radians, the angles may equally well be expressed in degrees.

Similarly, we may deduce that

$$B+C-A < \pi \qquad .... \qquad .... \qquad .... \qquad .... \qquad .... \qquad (2)$$
$$\text{and } C+A-B < \pi \qquad .... \qquad .... \qquad .... \qquad .... \qquad .... \qquad (3)$$

Now suppose that the primitive triangle is right angled at C.

It follows from (1) that $A + B < \dfrac{3\pi}{2}$, i.e. **in any right angled triangle, the sum of the three angles must be less than four right angles.**
... ... N.B.

Also, from (3) it follows that $A - B < \dfrac{\pi}{2}$ i.e. **the difference of the oblique angles of any right angled triangle is less than a right angle.**
... ... N.B.

(*d*) Consider the following numerical example.

Example 1.

In a spherical triangle ABC, given $A = 50°$, $C = 80°$, find the maximum possible value for B.

From the first of the three theorems given above, the difference of the two known angles must be less than the supplement of the third (unknown) angle. Hence

$$C - A < 180° - B$$
i.e. $\qquad B < 180° - 80° + 50° < 150°,$

that is, B must be less than 150°.

---

47. USE OF SUPPLEMENTAL THEOREM IN IDENTITIES.

It is not possible to lay down any hard and fast rules for this. In general, however, it is better to work in the primitive triangle. The supplemental theorem should therefore be used to clear the expression of any parts which are in the polar triangle. An example or two will make this clear.

Also it should be borne in mind that we may use any of the formulae of plane trigonometry which are not specificially related to the plane triangle. For instance,

$$\sin 2A = 2 \sin A \cos A$$
$$\cos (A+b) = \cos A \cos b - \sin A \sin b$$

etc., etc., are

simply formulae relating to angles, and they can be applied in spherical trigonometry just as in plane—and equally with big letters or small, since b of course, although the "length of a side", is in reality an angle, as we know.

Transformation of "sums into products" is particularly important, e.g. $\sin A + \sin B =$ twice sine half sum cos half difference, and so on.

As regards spherical formulae, all the identities we shall be dealing with in this chapter may be proved solely by the use of formulae already in our possession, chiefly:—

1. Cosine formula.
   $\cos a = \cos b \cos c + \sin b \sin c \cos A$, and similarly
   for $\cos b$ and $\cos c$.

2. By transposing the cosine formula, we get
   $\cos A = \dfrac{\cos a - \cos b \cos c}{\sin b \sin c}$, and similarly for $\cos B$ and $\cos C$.
   Use this to get "big letters into small ones"

3. The derived forms,
   $\cos a = \dfrac{\cos B \cos C + \cos A}{\sin B \sin C}$, and similarly for $\cos b$ and $\cos c$
   Use this to get "small letters into big ones"

4. Sine formula, Napier's Rules, together with all relevant formulae of plane trigonometry.

5. The geometrical properties of the sphere and spherical triangles.

The reader must be prepared to find these identities difficult at first. He must be prepared to use large sheets of paper!

NOTE: *All the following examples should be worked through in full by the student. Their purpose is to develop reasoning power, with the ability to thread one's way through an involved argument towards a required conclusion, and to provide practice in the manipulation of sometimes cumbersome expressions. All three are essential in the 'proofs' which form an important part of any mathematics course.*

48. IDENTITIES OF MODERATE DIFFICULTY.

Example 2.

If b be the side of an equilateral triangle BCD, and b' that of its polar triangle, show that $\cos \dfrac{b}{2} \cos \dfrac{b'}{2} = \dfrac{1}{2}$

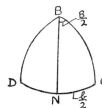

Take the left hand side, and clear it of any terms which relate to the polar triangle.

$$\text{L.H.S.} = \cos \frac{b}{2} \cos \frac{180 - B}{2}$$

$$= \cos \frac{b}{2} \sin \frac{B}{2} \qquad \dots \qquad \dots \qquad \dots \qquad (1)$$

In $\triangle BCD$, drop perp. BN, which also bisects the base.

Then by Napier's rules in BCN, $\cos \dfrac{B}{2} = \cos \dfrac{b}{2} \sin C$ (and $C = B$)

i.e. $\cos \dfrac{b}{2} = \dfrac{\cos \dfrac{B}{2}}{\sin B}$ and substituting

in (1), L.H.S. $= \dfrac{\sin \dfrac{B}{2} \cos \dfrac{B}{2}}{\sin B} = \dfrac{\sin \dfrac{B}{2} \cos \dfrac{B}{2}}{2 \sin \dfrac{B}{2} \cos \dfrac{B}{2}}$ (using $A.7$) $= \dfrac{1}{2}$

Hence $\cos \dfrac{b}{2} \cos \dfrac{b'}{2} = \dfrac{1}{2}$

Example 3.

If the corresponding angles of a triangle PZX and its polar triangle are equal, prove that
$$\sec^2 p + \sec^2 z + \sec^2 x - 2 \sec p \sec z \sec x = 1$$

"The corresponding angles are equal," that is, $P = P'$ etc. But $P' = 180 - p$, and so $P = 180 - p$. Now take the cosine formula:—
$$\cos p = \cos z \cos x + \sin z \sin x \cos P \qquad \text{and so,}$$
$$\cos p = \cos z \cos x - \sin z \sin x \cos p$$
Dividing through by $\cos z \cos x$

$$\frac{\cos p}{\cos z \cos x} = 1 - \tan z \tan x \cos p$$

$$\tan z \tan x = \frac{1}{\cos p} - \frac{1}{\cos z \cos x}$$

$$\tan z \tan x = \sec p - \sec z \sec x$$
Squaring both sides
$$\tan^2 z \tan^2 x = \sec^2 p - 2 \sec p \sec z \sec x + \sec^2 z \sec^2 x$$
and using $A.1$,
$$(\sec^2 z - 1)(\sec^2 x - 1) = \sec^2 p - 2 \sec p \sec z \sec x + \sec^2 z \sec^2 x$$
$$-\sec^2 x - \sec^2 z + 1 = \sec^2 p - 2 \sec p \sec z \sec x$$
i.e. $\sec^2 p + \sec^2 z + \sec^2 x - 2 \sec p \sec z \sec x = 1$

Example 4.

In a spherical triangle ABC, given that
$$\sin \tfrac{1}{2} (a+b) \sin \frac{C}{2} = \cos \tfrac{1}{2} (A-B) \sin \frac{c}{2},$$

prove that

$$\sin\frac{1}{2}(A+B)\cos\frac{c}{2} = \cos\frac{1}{2}(a-b)\cos\frac{C}{2}$$

L.H.S. $=\left(\sin\frac{a}{2}\cos\frac{b}{2}+\cos\frac{a}{2}\sin\frac{b}{2}\right)\sin\frac{C}{2}$ and by the supplemental theorem,

$$=\left(\sin\frac{180-A}{2}\cos\frac{180-B}{2}+\cos\frac{180-A}{2}\sin\frac{180-B}{2}\right)\sin\frac{180-C}{2}$$

$$=\left(\cos\frac{A}{2}\sin\frac{B}{2}+\sin\frac{A}{2}\cos\frac{B}{2}\right)\cos\frac{c}{2} \quad \text{(and using A.4)}$$

$$=\sin\frac{1}{2}(A+B)\cos\frac{c}{2}.$$ By proceeding similarly with the

R.H.S., the identity is proved.

Example 5.

The sides of a spherical triangle are all quadrants and x, y, z are the arcs joining any point P within the triangle to the angular points. Prove that

$$\cos^2 x+\cos^2 y+\cos^2 z=1.$$

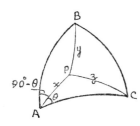

If the sides are all quadrants, it follows from the geometry of the sphere that the angles must all be 90°.

The figure illustrates the problem.

In $\triangle PAC$, in which $AC=90°$, by Napier's rules,

$$\cos z=\sin x \cos\theta \quad \dots \quad \dots \quad (1)$$

In $\triangle PAB$, similarly

$$\cos y=\sin x \sin\theta \quad \dots \quad \dots \quad (2)$$

Squaring and adding

$$\cos^2 z+\cos^2 y=\sin^2 x\ (\cos^2\theta+\sin^2\theta)$$
$$\cos^2 z+\cos^2 y=1-\cos^2 x \quad \dots \quad \dots \quad \text{(using A.1)}$$

i.e. $\cos^2 x+\cos^2 y+\cos^2 z=1$

Example 6.

From the fundamental cosine formula, prove that, in a spherical triangle PXZ,

$$\text{hav } P=\text{cosec } z \text{ cosec } x\sqrt{\text{hav }[p+(z\sim x)]\ \text{hav }[p-(z\sim x)]}$$

(This is known as the "half log haversine" formula and was at one time used in sight reduction. Though it is no longer so used, its proof provides a useful exercise.)

We have (see proof of nat. hav. formula in para. 17.)

$\cos p = \cos z \cos x + \sin z \sin x \cos P$,

and since hav $P = \frac{1}{2}(1 - \cos P)$

$\cos p = \cos z \cos x + \sin z \sin x (1 - 2 \text{ hav } P)$

$\cos p = \cos (z \sim x) - 2 \sin z \sin x \text{ hav } P$

i.e. $2 \sin z \sin x \text{ hav } P = \cos (z \sim x) - \cos p$, and using A.8

$2 \sin z \sin x \text{ hav } P = 2 \sin \frac{1}{2} [p + (z \sim x)] \sin \frac{1}{2} [p - (z \sim x)]$ (1)

Now by definition.

$$\text{hav } A = \frac{1}{2}(1 - \cos A) = \sin^2 \frac{A}{2} \qquad \text{using A.11, and so}$$

$$\sin \frac{p + (z \sim x)}{2} = \sqrt{\text{hav } [p + (z \sim x)]}$$

$$\sin \frac{p - (z \sim x)}{2} = \sqrt{\text{hav } [p - (z \sim x)]} \quad \text{and substituting in (1),}$$

$$\text{hav } P = \text{cosec } z \text{ cosec } x \sqrt{\text{hav } [p + (z \sim x)] \text{ hav } [p - (z \sim x)]}$$

Example 7.

If P is any point within the triangle ABC, and arcs be drawn from the corners A, B and C through P meeting the opposite sides in X, Y and Z respectively, prove that

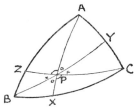

$$\frac{\sin BX \sin CY \sin AZ}{\sin CX \sin AY \sin BZ} = 1$$

The conditions are as illustrated.

In triangles BPX and CPX,

$$\frac{\sin BX}{\sin BP} = \frac{\sin \angle BPX}{\sin \angle BXP} \quad \text{and} \quad \frac{\sin CX}{\sin CP} = \frac{\sin \angle CPX}{\sin \angle CXP}$$

and dividing, (and since $\angle BXP$ and $\angle CXP$ are supplements)

$$\frac{\sin BX \sin CP}{\sin BP \sin CX} = \frac{\sin \angle BPX}{\sin \angle CPX}$$

$$\frac{\sin BX}{\sin CX} = \frac{\sin \angle BPX \sin BP}{\sin \angle CPX \sin CP} \quad \cdots \quad \cdots \quad \cdots \quad \cdots \quad (1)$$

Similarly, $\dfrac{\sin CY}{\sin AY} = \dfrac{\sin \angle CPY \sin CP}{\sin \angle APY \sin AP}$ $\cdots$ $\cdots$ $\cdots$ (2)

and $\dfrac{\sin AZ}{\sin BZ} = \dfrac{\sin \angle APZ \sin AP}{\sin \angle BPZ \sin BP}$ $\cdots$ $\cdots$ $\cdots$ (3)

Whence, multiplying $(1) \times (2) \times (3)$, we get

$$\frac{\sin BX \sin CY \sin AZ}{\sin CX \sin AY \sin BZ} = 1 \qquad \dots \qquad \dots \qquad \dots \qquad (4)$$

Corrollary:—Since P is any point, the converse is also true, i.e. if the relationship given at (4) can be shown to be true for any points X, Y, Z, then AX, BY, CZ must be concurrent.

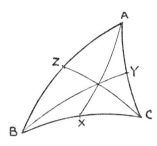

Hence, if X, Y, Z are the mid-points respectively, clearly

$$\frac{\sin BX \sin CY \sin AZ}{\sin CX \sin AY \sin BZ} = 1$$

$\therefore AX$, BY, CZ are concurrent.

(See para. 14, (j).

EXERCISE 4.—IDENTITIES OF MODERATE DIFFICULTY.

1. In a spherical triangle ABC, given $C = 48°$, $B = 72°$, find the maximum possible value for A.

2. If P is an angle of an equilateral spherical triangle and P' an angle of its polar triangle show that
   $$\cos P \cos P' = \cos P + \cos P'$$

3. If A be an angle of an equilateral spherical triangle and A' an angle in its polar triangle, prove that
   $$\text{hav } A \text{ hav } A' = \text{hav } 60°.$$

4. In a spherical triangle PAB, if $p + a + b = 180°$, prove that
   $$\text{hav } P = \cot a \cot b.$$

5. Given that PZX is an equilateral spherical triangle, prove that

   (a) $\cos P = \dfrac{\cos p}{1 + \cos p}$ $\qquad$ (b) $\sec \dfrac{x}{2} \operatorname{cosec} \dfrac{X}{2} = 2$

   (c) $\tan^2 \dfrac{x}{2} = 1 - 2 \cos X$ $\quad (d)$ $1 + 2 \cos p = \cot^2 \dfrac{P}{2}$

   (e) $\sec Z - \sec z = 1$.

6. In a spherical triangle ABC, if $a+c=90°$, prove that

(a) $\cos b = \sin 2c \cos^2 \dfrac{B}{2}$

(b) $(\cos c + \sin c) \sin B = 2 \cos^2 \dfrac{b}{2} \sin (A+C)$

7. The sides of a triangle are all quadrants and P is any point within it. Given that if x, y, z are the arcs joining P to the angular points then $\cos^2 x + \cos^2 y + \cos^2 z = 1$, show that, if α, β, γ are the perpendiculars from P on to the three sides, then $\sin^2 \alpha + \sin^2 \beta + \sin^2 \gamma = 1$.

8. In a spherical triangle PZX, PX is a quadrant and ZN is drawn perpendicular to PX. Prove that
$$\cot^2 ZN = \cot^2 P + \cot^2 X$$

9. In a spherical triangle ABC, given that

$$\sin \frac{A-B}{2} \sin \frac{c}{2} = \sin \frac{a-b}{2} \cos \frac{C}{2} \text{ , prove with}$$

the aid of the co-lunar triangle that

$$\cos \frac{A+B}{2} \cos \frac{c}{2} = \cos \frac{a+b}{2} \sin \frac{C}{2} \text{ , where } A \text{ is the angle of}$$

the lune.

10. In a spherical triangle ABC, if M is the midpoint of BC, prove that
$$2 \cos \tfrac{1}{2} BC \cos AM = \cos AB + \cos AC.$$

11. In the spherical triangle ABC, right angled at A, prove that

(a) $\cos (b+c) + \cos (b-c) = 2 \cos a$

(b) $\tan^2 \dfrac{B}{2} = \dfrac{\sin (a-c)}{\sin (a+c)}$

(c) $\sin (a+b) \sin (a-b) = \sin^2 c \cos^2 b$

(d) $\tan^2 \dfrac{c}{2} = \tan \dfrac{a+b}{2} \tan \dfrac{a-b}{2}$

12. If ABC be a spherical triangle and AD the perpendicular from A on to BC, show that
$$\frac{\tan BD}{\tan CD} = \frac{\tan \angle BAD}{\tan \angle CAD}$$

13. In a spherical triangle ABC, if angle A = side c, prove that
$$\sin (B-b) = \sin b \sin B \cos A \cot A$$

14. ABC is a spherical triangle right angled at B. AN and CM are drawn perpendicular to any great circle passing through B. Prove that

$$\frac{\tan^2 BN}{\tan^2 AB} + \frac{\tan^2 BM}{\tan^2 BC} = 1$$

15. In a spherical triangle PAB, prove that

$$\sin (a+b) = \sin p \cos A + 2 \sin a \cos b \cos^2 \frac{P}{2}$$

16. In a quadrantal triangle ABC, $a = 90°$. Prove that

$$\tan \frac{b}{2} = \frac{\sin A - \cos B \sin C}{\sin B}$$

17. In a spherical triangle PQR, right angled at R, prove that

(a) $\sin (r-p) = \tan q \cos r \tan \dfrac{Q}{2}$

(b) $2 \sin Q \cos^2 \left(\dfrac{\pi}{4} + \dfrac{r}{2} \right) = \sin Q - \sin q$

18. In a spherical triangle ABC, if $b = c$ prove that

(a) $\tan c \operatorname{cosec} \dfrac{a}{2} \cot C = \sec \dfrac{A}{2}$

(b) $\sin^2 C \cos^2 \dfrac{a}{2} \sin^2 c = \sin^2 c - \sin^2 \dfrac{a}{2}$

19. In the spherical triangle ABC, show that

$$\frac{\sin (B+C)}{\sin A} = \operatorname{cosec} a \ (\cos C \sin b + \cos B \sin c)$$

20. A lune of angle θ is divided into two isosceles triangles, one being twice the area of the other. If the angles at the base in the smaller triangle are α, show that

$$\alpha = \frac{\pi}{2} - \frac{\theta}{6}$$

49. THE ''HALF ANGLE FORMULAE''·

These are usually stated as follows:—

$$\sin \frac{A}{2} = \sqrt{\frac{\sin (s-b) \sin (s-c)}{\sin b \sin c}} \qquad \cdot\cdot \qquad \cdot\cdot \quad IXa$$

$$\cos \frac{A}{2} = \sqrt{\frac{\sin s \sin (s-a)}{\sin b \sin c}} \qquad \cdot\cdot \qquad \cdot\cdot \quad IXb$$

$$\tan \frac{A}{2} = \sqrt{\frac{\sin (s-b) \sin (s-c)}{\sin s \ \text{son} \ (s-a)}} \qquad \cdot\cdot \qquad \cdot\cdot \quad IXc$$

where $s = \frac{1}{2}(a+b+c)$

Proof of IX*a*

From A.11 we have

$$2\sin^2\frac{A}{2} = 1 - \cos A$$

$$= 1 - \frac{\cos a - \cos b \cos c}{\sin b \sin c}$$

$$= \frac{\sin b \sin c + \cos b \cos c - \cos a}{\sin b \sin c} \quad \text{and using A.5}$$

$$= \frac{\cos(b-c) - \cos a}{\sin b \sin c} \quad \text{....} \quad \text{and using A.8}$$

$$= \frac{2\sin\frac{1}{2}(b-c+a)\sin\frac{1}{2}(a-b+c)}{\sin b \sin c}$$

Now if $a+b+c = 2s$

  then $a+b-c = 2s-2c$

  and $a+c-b = 2s-2b$, so, substituting,

$$2\sin^2\frac{A}{2} = \frac{2\sin\frac{1}{2}(2s-2c)\sin\frac{1}{2}(2s-2b)}{\sin b \sin c}$$

$$\sin^2\frac{A}{2} = \frac{\sin(s-c)\sin(s-b)}{\sin b \sin c}, \text{ or}$$

$$\sin\frac{A}{2} = \sqrt{\frac{\sin(s-b)\sin(s-c)}{\sin b \sin c}} \quad \text{....} \quad \text{....} \quad \text{IX}a$$

Similarly, we have, from A.11,

$2\cos^2\dfrac{A}{2} = 1 + \cos A$, and by a precisely similar method IX b may be proved. (The reader is advised to work this through for himself.)

Finally,

$$\tan\frac{A}{2} = \frac{\sin\dfrac{A}{2}}{\cos\dfrac{A}{2}}, \text{ from which IX } c \text{ follows}$$

Although perhaps not used very frequently, nevertheless, when they are required, they are particularly useful formulae, and they should be known.

50. THE "HALF SIDE FORMULAE".

These are less commonly employed than the half angle formulae just considered. However, let us work through one as a useful exercise.

To prove that

$$\sin \frac{a}{2} = \sqrt{-\frac{\cos S \cos (S-A)}{\sin B \sin C}} \quad \dots \quad \dots \quad \dots \quad Xa$$

where $2S = A+B+C$

From VIII a in para. 45, we have,

$$\cos a = \frac{\cos A + \cos B \cos C}{\sin B \sin C} \quad \text{and therefore}$$

$$1 - \cos a = \frac{\sin B \sin C - \cos A - \cos B \cos C}{\sin B \sin C}$$

$$2 \sin^2 \frac{a}{2} = -\frac{\cos A + \cos (B+C)}{\sin B \sin C}$$

$$2 \sin^2 \frac{a}{2} = -\frac{2 \cos \frac{1}{2} (A+B+C) \cos \frac{1}{2} (B+C-A)}{\sin B \sin C}$$

Now if $A+B+C = 2S$

$$B+C-A = 2S - 2A \quad \text{and substituting, we have}$$

$$\sin^2 \frac{a}{2} = -\frac{\cos S \cos (S-A)}{\sin B \sin C} \quad , \quad \text{that is}$$

$$\boldsymbol{\sin \frac{a}{2} = \sqrt{-\frac{\cos S \cos (S-A)}{\sin B \sin C}}} \quad \dots \quad \dots \quad Xa$$

Similarly, it may be shown that

$$\boldsymbol{\cos \frac{a}{2} = \sqrt{\frac{\cos (S-B) \cos (S-C)}{\sin B \sin C}}} \quad \dots \quad Xb$$

and $\boldsymbol{\tan \frac{a}{2} = \sqrt{-\frac{\cos S \cos (S-A)}{\cos (S-B) \cos (S-C)}}} \quad \dots \quad Xc$

Note that the values of $\sin \frac{a}{2}$ and $\tan \frac{a}{2}$ are always real.

By para. 10 the sum of the three angles must always lie between 180° and 540°, and so S must always lie between 90° and 270° and therefore $\cos S$ is always negative.

F

Again, as we have seen (para. 13 a) in any triangle we must have $b+c>a$

i.e. $180°-B+180°-C>180°-A$

$-B-C+A>-180°$

$B+C-A<180°$

that is $2S-2A<180°$

$S-A<90°$ and so its cosine is always positive.

Similarly for $(S-B)$ and $(S-C)$.

51. HARDER IDENTITIES.

NOTE:—*Again, these should be worked through in full by the student.*

Example 8.

In a spherical triangle ABC, prove that

$$\frac{\sin (B+C)}{2 \sin A} = \frac{\cos \frac{1}{2} (b+c) \cos \frac{1}{2} (b-c)}{1+\cos a}$$

R.H.S. $= \dfrac{\cos b+\cos c}{2 (1+\cos a)}$, using A.9, and now "into big letters"

$$= \frac{\dfrac{\cos B+\cos C \cos A}{\sin C \sin A} + \dfrac{\cos C+\cos A \cos B}{\sin A \sin B}}{2 \left(1 + \dfrac{\cos A+\cos B \cos C}{\sin B \sin C} \right)}$$

$$= \frac{\dfrac{\sin B (\cos B+\cos C \cos A)+\sin C (\cos C+\cos A \cos B)}{\sin A \sin B \sin C}}{\dfrac{2 (\sin B \sin C+\cos A+\cos B \cos C)}{\sin B \sin C}}$$

$$= \frac{\sin B \cos B+\sin B \cos C \cos A+\sin C \cos C+\sin C \cos A \cos B}{2 \sin A [\cos (B-C)+\cos A]}$$

.... (using A.5)

$$= \frac{\frac{1}{2} \sin 2B+\frac{1}{2} \sin 2C+\cos A \sin (B+C)}{2 \sin A [\cos (B-C)+\cos A]}$$ .... using A.7 and A.4

$$= \frac{\sin (B+C) \cos (B-C)+\cos A \sin (B+C)}{2 \sin A [\cos (B-C)+\cos A]}$$ .... using A.8

$$= \frac{\sin (B+C) [\cos (B-C)+\cos A]}{2 \sin A [\cos (B-C)+\cos A]} = \frac{\sin (B+C)}{2 \sin A} = \text{L.H.S.}$$

NOTE:—Though not necessarily the shortest, this is a particularly valuable proof as it brings in so many important points. The reader may care to try his skill on the L.H.S. which, by expanding the numerator, then using sine formula and cosine formula, can be got entirely into small letters. The rest follows.

Example 9.

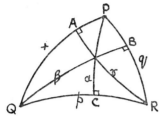

In the triangle PQR, if α, β, γ be the perpendiculars, respectively, on to the opposite sides, show that $\sin \alpha \sin p = \sin \gamma \sin r = \sin \beta \sin q$

The figure illustrates the problem.
In $\triangle PRA$, by Napier's rules
$$\sin \gamma = \sin P \sin PR \qquad \dots \quad (1)$$
In $\triangle PRC$, by Napier's rules
$$\sin \alpha = \sin R \sin PR \qquad \dots \quad (2)$$

and from $(1) \div (2)$

$$\frac{\sin \gamma}{\sin \alpha} = \frac{\sin P}{\sin R} \quad \dots \qquad \dots \qquad \dots \qquad \dots \qquad \dots \quad (3)$$

By sine formula,

$$\frac{\sin p}{\sin P} = \frac{\sin r}{\sin R}$$

i.e. $\dfrac{\sin p}{\sin r} = \dfrac{\sin P}{\sin R}$ and substituting in (3)

$$\frac{\sin \gamma}{\sin \alpha} = \frac{\sin p}{\sin r}$$

that is $\sin \alpha \sin p = \sin \gamma \sin r$. Similarly it may be shown that $\sin \gamma \sin r = \sin \beta \sin q$.

In the same triangle show that

$$\sin \beta \sin q = \sqrt{1 - \cos^2 p - \cos^2 q - \cos^2 r + 2 \cos p \cos q \cos r}$$
By Napier's rules in $\triangle PQB$,
$\sin \beta = \sin r \sin P$

$$= \sin r \sqrt{1 - \cos^2 P} \text{ and } \cos P = \frac{\cos p - \cos r \cos q}{\sin r \sin q}$$

so $\sin \beta = \sin r \sqrt{1 - \left(\dfrac{\cos p - \cos r \cos q}{\sin r \sin q} \right)^2}$

$$= \sin r \sqrt{\frac{\sin^2 r \sin^2 q - \cos^2 p - \cos^2 r \cos^2 q + 2 \cos p \cos r \cos q}{\sin^2 r \sin^2 q}}$$

$\sin \beta \sin q$
$$= \sqrt{(1 - \cos^2 r)(1 - \cos^2 q) - \cos^2 p - \cos^2 r \cos^2 q + 2 \cos p \cos r \cos q}$$

$\sin \beta \sin q = \sqrt{1 - \cos^2 r - \cos^2 q - \cos^2 p + 2 \cos p \cos r \cos q}$

Example 10.

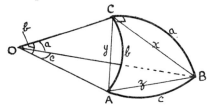

In the triangle ABC, right angled at C, $a=b$. If the chords to the sides a, b, c are respectively x, y, z, and R is the radius of the sphere, prove that

$$z^2 = y^2 \left(2 - \frac{y^2}{2R^2}\right)$$

The figure illustrates the problem.

In the plane $\triangle OAC$, using A.12, we have

$$y^2 = R^2 + R^2 - 2R^2 \cos b \qquad \dots \qquad \dots \qquad \dots \qquad (1)$$

and in $\triangle OAB$, $\quad z^2 = R^2 + R^2 - 2R^2 \cos c \qquad \dots \qquad \dots \qquad \dots \qquad (2)$

and in $\triangle OBC$ $\quad x^2 = R^2 + R^2 - 2R^2 \cos a \qquad \dots \qquad \dots \qquad \dots \qquad (3)$

By Napier's rules in spher. $\triangle ABC$

$$\cos c = \cos b \cos a \qquad \dots \qquad \dots \qquad \dots \qquad (4)$$

$(1) \div (2)$ gives $\dfrac{y^2 - 2R^2}{z^2 - 2R^2} = \dfrac{\cos b}{\cos c} = \dfrac{1}{\cos a}$ (from 4),

and substituting for $\cos a$ from (3) we have

$$\frac{y^2 - 2R^2}{z^2 - 2R^2} = \frac{2R^2}{2R^2 - x^2} \qquad \text{Since } a = b, \therefore x = y,$$

and so $\quad \dfrac{y^2 - 2R^2}{z^2 - 2R^2} = \dfrac{2R^2}{2R^2 - y^2}$ and by reducing this,

we obtain $\qquad z^2 = y^2 \left(2 - \dfrac{y^2}{2R^2}\right)$

Example 11.

In a spherical triangle PQR, right angled at R, θ is the angle between the chords PR and QR.

Prove that $\cos \theta = \sin \dfrac{p}{2} \sin \dfrac{q}{2}$

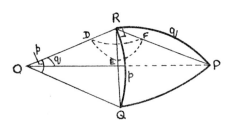

The figure illustrates $\triangle PQR$, on a sphere whose centre is O. About R as centre describe a sphere of any desired radius, meeting RO, RQ, RP in D, E, F.

Then $\angle EDF$ is the inclination of planes ORQ, ORP and is $\therefore$ equal to $\angle R$ i.e. $= 90°$.

Also EF is the measure of θ, the angle between the chords.
So by Napier's rules in $\triangle DEF$, right angled at D,
$$\cos \theta = \cos DE \cos DF \qquad \text{....} \qquad \text{....} \qquad \text{....} \qquad (1)$$
Also, plane $\triangle ORQ$ is isosceles, and since DE is the measure of $\angle ORQ$,
$$\therefore DE = \tfrac{1}{2}(180° - p) = 90° - \frac{p}{2}$$

Similarly, plane $\triangle ORP$ is isosceles, and since DF is the measure of $\angle ORP$,
$$\therefore DF = \tfrac{1}{2}(180° - q) = 90° - \frac{q}{2}$$

Substituting in (1) we have
$$\cos \theta = \cos \left(90° - \frac{p}{2}\right) \cos \left(90° - \frac{q}{2}\right)$$
$$\cos \theta = \sin \frac{p}{2} \sin \frac{q}{2}$$

Example 12.

In a quadrantal triangle ABC, $a = \dfrac{\pi}{2}$. Prove that
$$\tan \tfrac{1}{2}(a+b+c-\pi) = \tan \frac{B}{2} \tan \frac{C}{2}$$

L.H.S. $= \tan \tfrac{1}{2}\left(b+c-\dfrac{\pi}{2}\right) = \tan\left(\dfrac{b+c}{2} - \dfrac{\pi}{4}\right)$ \qquad and using 1·6

$$= \frac{\tan\dfrac{b+c}{2} - 1}{\tan\dfrac{b+c}{2} + 1} = \frac{\sin\dfrac{b+c}{2} - \cos\dfrac{b+c}{2}}{\sin\dfrac{b+c}{2} + \cos\dfrac{b+c}{2}} \qquad \text{....} \qquad \text{....} \qquad (1)$$

R.H.S.   From IX c,
$$\tan \frac{B}{2} \tan \frac{C}{2} = \sqrt{\frac{\sin (s-a)\,\sin (s-c)}{\sin s \, \sin (s-b)} \cdot \frac{\sin (s-a)\,\sin (s-b)}{\sin s \, \sin (s-c)}}$$

$$= \frac{\sin (s-a)}{\sin s} \quad \text{Now } s = \frac{a}{2} + \frac{b}{2} + \frac{c}{2}, \text{ so substituting,}$$

$$\text{R.H.S.} = \frac{\sin \left(\dfrac{b+c}{2} - \dfrac{a}{2}\right)}{\sin \left(\dfrac{b+c}{2} + \dfrac{a}{2}\right)}$$

$$= \frac{\sin\dfrac{b+c}{2} \cos\dfrac{a}{2} - \cos\dfrac{b+c}{2} \sin\dfrac{a}{2}}{\sin\dfrac{b+c}{2} \cos\dfrac{a}{2} + \cos\dfrac{b+c}{2} \sin\dfrac{a}{2}} \qquad \text{and } \frac{a}{2} = \frac{\pi}{4} \qquad \text{i.e.}$$

$$\sin \frac{a}{2} = \cos \frac{a}{2}$$

whence R.H.S. $= \dfrac{\sin\dfrac{b+c}{2} - \cos\dfrac{b+c}{2}}{\sin\dfrac{b+c}{2} + \cos\dfrac{b+c}{2}}$ $=$ L.H.S., as at (1)

Example 13.

The d. long. between two places in the same latitude L is $2\,\theta$ radians. Show that, between the two places,

$$\frac{\text{distance along the parallel}}{\text{distance along the G.C.}} = \frac{\theta \cos L}{\alpha}\text{ , where } \alpha \text{ is in radians}$$

and $\sin \alpha = \cos L \sin \theta$

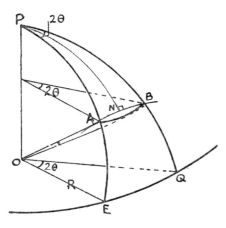

Let radius of earth be R. (assumed spherical). A and B are the two places.

Distance between their meridians along the Equator, $EQ = R.2\,\theta$ and so distance along the parallel, $AB = 2\,R\,\theta \cos L$ (1)

Drop perp. PN, which ∴ bisects AB and also bisects $\angle APB$.

G.C. distance $= 2.$ AN, and in $\triangle PAN$, $\sin AN = \cos L \sin \theta$

∴ from equation given, arc AN must equal α, i.e. $\angle AOB = 2\,\alpha$, and length of arc AB, that is, the G.C. distance $= R.\,2\,\alpha$ ....   (2)

Hence $\dfrac{\text{distance along parallel}}{\text{distance along G.C.}} = \dfrac{(1)}{(2)} = \dfrac{\theta \cos L}{\alpha}$

EXERCISE 5.—HARDER IDENTITIES.

1. From the fundamental cosine formula, prove that in a spherical triangle ABC,

    vers $a =$ vers $(b-c) + \sin b \sin c$ vers A

2. In a spherical triangle PQR, prove that

    $$\frac{\cos Q + \cos R}{1 - \cos P} = \frac{\sin (q+r)}{\sin p}$$

3. In a spherical triangle ABC, if N is the midpoint of AC, prove that

    $$\cos BN = \cos \tfrac{1}{2}\,(a+c)\,\cos \tfrac{1}{2}\,(a-c)\,\sec \frac{b}{2}$$

4. In the navigational triangle PZX in which
    z=polar distance, p=zenith distance, x=co-lat, $\angle P$=hour
    angle, deduce from the fundamental cosine formula that
    hav P=sec l cosec z cos Q sin $(Q-a)$ where
    l=latitude, a=altitude and $Q=\frac{1}{2}$ $(a+l+$ $z)$.

5. In the spherical triangle ABC, if
    $$\sin s = \frac{\sin (s-b) \sin (s-c)}{\sin (s-a)} \quad \text{where}$$
    $s=\frac{1}{2}$ $(a+b+c)$, prove that the triangle is right angled at A.

6. In a spherical triangle PQR, N is the midpoint of QR.
    Prove that $\cos PN = \dfrac{\cos \frac{1}{2} (r+q) \cos \frac{1}{2} (r-q)}{\cos \frac{1}{2} p}$

7. The area of a quadrantal spherical triangle ABC is one
    quarter the area of the sphere upon which it is described.
    If side c of the triangle=90°, prove that 2 cot B=tan A.

8. In a spherical triangle PQR in which α, β, γ be the perpendic-
    ulars, respectively on to the opposite sides, show that
    $\sin p \cos α=\sqrt{\cos^2 q+\cos^2 r-2 \cos p \cos q \cos r}$

9. If M be the midpoint of the base QR of a spherical triangle
    PQR, and N a point on the base such that angle $QPM=$
    angle RPN, prove that
    $$\frac{\sin QN}{\sin RN} = \frac{\sin^2 r}{\sin^2 q}$$

10. In a spherical triangle ABC, prove that
    $$\text{hav } A = \frac{\sin (s-b) \sin (s-c)}{\sin b \sin c}$$

    (NOTE:—This is known as the log haversine formula and was
    at one time used in sight reduction.)

11. In a spherical triangle ABC, prove that
    $$\frac{\sin (A-B)}{\sin \dfrac{C}{2} \cos \dfrac{C}{2}} = \frac{\cos b-\cos a}{\text{hav } c}$$

12. A lune whose angle is θ is divided into two isosceles triangles
    so that the area of one is twice the area of the other. If x
    is one of the equal sides in the smaller triangle, show that
    $$\cos x = \cot \frac{θ}{2} \tan \frac{θ}{6}$$

13. In a spherical triangle PZX, if $x+z$=90°, from the formula
    hav p=hav $(x-z)$+sin x sin z hav P, deduce that cos
    p=sin x cos x $(1+\cos P)$.

14. Two positions A and B are in the same latitude L and their d. long. is θ radians. Prove that the distance between them along the parallel is greater than the great circle distance by

$$2R \left(\frac{\theta}{2} \cos L - \alpha \right) \text{ where } R \text{ is the radius of the earth and}$$

$$\sin \alpha = \sin \frac{\theta}{2} \cos L.$$

15. ABC is an equilateral spherical triangle and P is the pole of the circumscribing circle. If X is any point within the triangle, prove that

$$3 \cos PB \cos PX = \cos AX + \cos BX + \cos CX$$

16. In the spherical triangle PQR the bisector of angle P meets QR in N, and M is the midpoint of QR. If $r > q$ prove that

$$\tan MN = \tan \frac{p}{2} \, \frac{\sin r - \sin q}{\sin r + \sin q}$$

17. In a spherical triangle ABC, $b + c = 60°$. Prove that

$$\tfrac{1}{2} \left(4 \cos^2 \frac{a}{2} - 3 \right) \tan^2 \frac{A}{2} = \cos (b-c) - \cos a.$$

18. In a spherical triangle ABC, right angled at A, $AB - AC$ and θ is the angle between chords AB and AC.
    Prove that

$$2 \cos \theta = 1 - \cos b$$

19. If D and E are the midpoints of sides PQ and PR in the spherical triangle PQR, and DE produced meets QR produced in F, prove that

$$\sin FD \cos \frac{r}{2} = \sin FE \cos \frac{q}{2}$$

20. In a spherical triangle ABC, show that

$$\sin A = \frac{2\sqrt{\sin s \sin (s-a) \sin (s-b) \sin (s-c)}}{\sin b \sin c}$$

21. A, B and C in that order are three points on a Great Circle and Q is any other point on the sphere. Prove that
    $$\cos QA \sin BC + \cos QC \sin AB = \cos QB \sin AC$$

22. Using the fundamental cosine formula for $\cos b$, show that in a spherical triangle ABC
    $$\sin a \cos B = \cos b \sin c - \sin b \cos c \cos A$$

CHAPTER VI

FORMULAE

In this chapter we propose to give a few formulae which, although not in general use, are nevertheless occasionally required by the specialist.

52. DELAMBRE'S ANALOGIES.

These are four in number, namely:—

$$\frac{\sin \frac{1}{2}(A+B)}{\cos \frac{1}{2} C} = \frac{\cos \frac{1}{2}(a-b)}{\cos \frac{1}{2} c} \qquad \cdots \qquad \cdots \quad XIa$$

$$\frac{\sin \frac{1}{2}(A-B)}{\cos \frac{1}{2} C} = \frac{\sin \frac{1}{2}(a-b)}{\sin \frac{1}{2} c} \qquad \cdots \qquad \cdots \quad XIb$$

$$\frac{\cos \frac{1}{2}(A+B)}{\sin \frac{1}{2} C} = \frac{\cos \frac{1}{2}(a+b)}{\cos \frac{1}{2} c} \qquad \cdots \qquad \cdots \quad XIc$$

$$\frac{\cos \frac{1}{2}(A-B)}{\sin \frac{1}{2} C} = \frac{\sin \frac{1}{2}(a+b)}{\sin \frac{1}{2} c} \qquad \cdots \qquad \cdots \quad XId$$

Proof of XI a.

$$\sin \tfrac{1}{2}(A+B) = \sin \frac{A}{2} \cos \frac{B}{2} + \cos \frac{A}{2} \sin \frac{B}{2} \text{ and by formulae IX}$$

$$= \sqrt{\frac{\sin(s-b)\sin(s-c)}{\sin b \sin c}} \cdot \sqrt{\frac{\sin s \sin(s-b)}{\sin a \sin c}}$$

$$+ \sqrt{\frac{\sin s \sin(s-a)}{\sin b \sin c}} \cdot \sqrt{\frac{\sin(s-a)\sin(s-c)}{\sin a \sin c}}$$

$$= \frac{\sin(s-b)}{\sin c} \sqrt{\frac{\sin s \sin(s-c)}{\sin a \sin b}} + \frac{\sin(s-a)}{\sin c} \sqrt{\frac{\sin s \sin(s-c)}{\sin a \sin b}}$$

$$\frac{\sin(s-b)}{\sin c} \cdot \cos \frac{C}{2} + \frac{\sin(s-a)}{\sin c} \cdot \cos \frac{C}{2} \qquad \text{i.e.}$$

$$\sin \tfrac{1}{2}(A+B) = \cos \frac{C}{2} \left(\frac{\sin(s-b)+\sin(s-a)}{\sin c} \right)$$

73

$$\frac{\sin \frac{1}{2}(A+B)}{\cos \frac{C}{2}} = \frac{\sin(s-b)+\sin(s-a)}{\sin c}$$

Now

$$s = \frac{a}{2} + \frac{b}{2} + \frac{c}{2}$$

$$s-b = \frac{a}{2} - \frac{b}{2} + \frac{c}{2}$$

$$s-a = \frac{b}{2} + \frac{c}{2} - \frac{a}{2}$$

and substituting,

$$\text{R.H.S.} = \frac{\sin\left(\frac{a}{2} - \frac{b}{2} + \frac{c}{2}\right) + \sin\left(\frac{b}{2} + \frac{c}{2} - \frac{a}{2}\right)}{\sin c}$$

and using A.8

$$= \frac{2 \sin \frac{1}{2} c \cos \frac{1}{2}(a-b)}{2 \sin \frac{c}{2} \cos \frac{c}{2}} = \frac{\cos \frac{1}{2}(a-b)}{\cos \frac{1}{2} c}$$

i.e. $$\frac{\sin \frac{1}{2}(A+B)}{\cos \frac{1}{2} C} = \frac{\cos \frac{1}{2}(a-b)}{\cos \frac{1}{2} c}$$ .... XI a.

The others may be proved by a similar method.

These formulae may occasionally be used in the solution of triangles where the data available is perhaps rather unorthodox. Consider the following:

Example 1.   In a spherical triangle ABC, $A=90°$ and $B+C=108°$ 04'. The perimeter of the triangle$=146°$ 02'. Find side a.

(Note that this could not be solved by any of the methods previously employed).

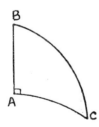

$B+C=108°\ 04'$
$2s=146°\ 02'$
$s=73°\ 01'$
By XI c, we have

$$\frac{\cos \frac{1}{2}(B+C)}{\sin \frac{1}{2} A} = \frac{\cos \frac{1}{2}(b+c)}{\cos \frac{1}{2} a}$$

and since $2s=a+b+c$

we have $\dfrac{\cos 54° \ 02'}{\sin 45°} = \dfrac{\cos \frac{1}{2} \ (2s-a)}{\cos \frac{1}{2} \ a}$

$$= \dfrac{\cos s \ \cos \dfrac{a}{2} + \sin s \ \sin \dfrac{a}{2}}{\cos \dfrac{a}{2}}.$$

$= \cos s + \sin s \ \tan \dfrac{a}{2}$ and solving this gives

$$\dfrac{a}{2} = 29° \ 23' \qquad \text{whence } a = 58° \ 46'.$$

53. NAPIER'S ANALOGIES.

These are also four in number and are as follows:—

$$\textbf{tan } \tfrac{1}{2} \ (A+B) = \dfrac{\textbf{cos } \frac{1}{2} \ (a-b)}{\textbf{cos } \frac{1}{2} \ (a+b)} \quad \textbf{cot} \dfrac{C}{2} \qquad .. \quad XIIa$$

$$\textbf{tan } \tfrac{1}{2} \ (A-B) = \dfrac{\textbf{sin } \frac{1}{2} \ (a-b)}{\textbf{sin } \frac{1}{2} \ (a+b)} \quad \textbf{cot} \dfrac{C}{2} \qquad .. \quad XIIb$$

$$\textbf{tan } \tfrac{1}{2} \ (a+b) = \dfrac{\textbf{cos } \frac{1}{2} \ (A-B)}{\textbf{cos } \frac{1}{2} \ (A+B)} \quad \textbf{tan } \dfrac{c}{2} \qquad .. \quad XIIc$$

$$\textbf{tan } \tfrac{1}{2} \ (a-b) = \dfrac{\textbf{sin } \frac{1}{2} \ (A-B)}{\textbf{sin } \frac{1}{2} \ (A+B)} \quad \textbf{tan } \dfrac{c}{2} \qquad .. \quad XIId$$

Before proceeding to prove one of them, let us remind ourselves of the following, which may be found in most textbooks on algebra.

If two quantities, a and b are in the same ratio as two other quantities x and y, that is, $\dfrac{a}{b} = \dfrac{x}{y}$ then:—

$\dfrac{a+b}{b} = \dfrac{x+y}{y}$, a process known as componendo, and

$\dfrac{a-b}{b} = \dfrac{x-y}{y}$, a process known as dividendo.

Now we know that $\dfrac{\sin A}{\sin a} = \dfrac{\sin B}{\sin b}$

Let each of these ratios $= m$.

Transposing, we have $\dfrac{\sin A}{\sin B} = \dfrac{\sin a}{\sin b}$

Then $\dfrac{\sin A + \sin B}{\sin B} = \dfrac{\sin a + \sin b}{\sin b}$

i.e. $\dfrac{\sin A + \sin B}{\sin a + \sin b} = \dfrac{\sin B}{\sin b} = m$ ....   (1)

and similarly

$\dfrac{\sin A - \sin B}{\sin a - \sin b} = \dfrac{\sin B}{\sin b} = m$ ....   (2)

Now to prove XII a.

From the previous chapter, by VIII a and VIII b we have
$$\cos A + \cos B \cos C = \sin B \sin C \cos a$$
and $\cos B + \cos A \cos C = \sin A \sin C \cos b$

From (1) $\sin B = m \sin b$ and similarly $\sin A = m \sin a$, so substituting in these two formulae, we have
$$\cos A + \cos B \cos C = m \sin C \sin b \cos a$$
and $\cos B + \cos A \cos C = m \sin C \sin a \cos b$ and adding
$(\cos A + \cos B) + \cos C (\cos A + \cos B) = m \sin C (\sin a \cos b + \cos a \sin b)$.

$(\cos A + \cos B)(1 + \cos C) = m \sin C \sin (a+b)$ ....   (3)

Dividing (1) by (3) we get

$\dfrac{\sin A + \sin B}{\cos A + \cos B} = \dfrac{\sin a + \sin b}{\sin (a+b)} \cdot \dfrac{1 + \cos C}{\sin C}$ and using $A.7$, $A.8$
                                                                                        and $A.11$,

$\dfrac{2 \sin \frac{1}{2}(A+B) \cos \frac{1}{2}(A-B)}{2 \cos \frac{1}{2}(A+B) \cos \frac{1}{2}(A-B)} = \dfrac{2 \sin \frac{1}{2}(a+b) \cos \frac{1}{2}(a-b)}{2 \sin \frac{1}{2}(a+b) \cos \frac{1}{2}(a+b)} \cdot$

$$\dfrac{2 \cos^2 \dfrac{C}{2}}{2 \sin \dfrac{C}{2} \cos \dfrac{C}{2}}$$

i.e. $\tan \tfrac{1}{2}(A+B) = \dfrac{\cos \frac{1}{2}(a-b)}{\cos \frac{1}{2}(a+b)} \cot \dfrac{C}{2}$ *XIIa.*

To prove XII b, divide (2) by (3) and proceed by a similar method.

Finally, to prove XII c and XII d, we may employ the usual polar triangle substitutions, $A = 180° - a'$ etc. in XII a and XII b.

Alternatively, they may be proved from first principles commencing with formulae I of chapter 2, namely

$$\cos a - \cos b \cos c = \sin b \sin c \cos A$$
and $\quad \cos b - \cos a \cos c = \sin a \sin c \cos B$

and proceeding on precisely similar lines to those given in the above proof for XII a. To deduce one of these for himself would be a useful exercise for the reader.

54. USE OF NAPIER'S ANALOGIES.

As in the example given in para. 52, Napier's Analogies have a somewhat restricted and specialized use. They are required, for instance, in the proof of the half convergency formula used in correcting great circle wireless bearings. They are difficult to remember, and your author has always preferred to avoid using them if possible. However:—

Example 2.

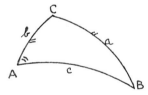

Given two sides and the angle opposite one of them—e.g. In the $\triangle ABC$, given a, b and A.

We could first use the sine formula to determine B, hoping we should be able to resolve the ambiguity which is always present when an angle is found through its sine (para. 20)

If this is not possible, then of course there are two solutions (the ambiguous case).

Having now a, b, A, B, we can use Napier's analogies XII a to find C, and XII c to find c.

This involves a good deal of work and is not to everyone's taste!

Alternatively, we could use the four-part formula to find C, though this is not too easy since C is an "inner".

Probably the best method would be to drop a perpendicular from C on to c, use Napier's Rules to find c and complete either by haversine formula or by further application of Napier's Rules.

Example 3.

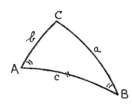

Given two angles and the side included between them:—e.g. In the $\triangle ABC$, given A, B, c.

Here again, whilst a direct solution may be obtained by using Napier's analogies XII c and XII a to find a and b, most readers will prefer to avoid a frontal assault!

Thus, we can use the four-part formula under quite favourable conditions (either b or a are both "outers").

Alternatively, since we have two angles and the included side in the primitive triangle, we would have two sides and the included angle in the polar triangle, which of course can be solved by haversine formula.

Example 4.

In a triangle ABC, $\angle B = 88°$, $\angle C = 36°$ and $a+b+c = 104°$. Find a.

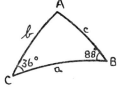

This is an unusual combination of data.

By XII c, we have

$$\tan \tfrac{1}{2}(b+c) = \frac{\cos \tfrac{1}{2}(B-C)}{\cos \tfrac{1}{2}(B+C)} \cdot \tan \frac{a}{2} \quad \text{....} \quad \text{....} \quad \text{....} \quad (1)$$

Also, $a+b+c = 104°$

$$\frac{b+c}{2} = 52° - \frac{a}{2} \qquad \text{and in (1)}$$

$$\tan\left(52° - \frac{a}{2}\right) = \frac{\cos 26°}{\cos 62°} \cdot \tan \frac{a}{2} \qquad \text{and putting } \tan \frac{a}{2} = t$$

$$52° = s$$

$$\text{and } \frac{\cos 26°}{\cos 62°} = A,$$

we have $\dfrac{\tan s - t}{1 + t \tan s} = A t$

$\tan s - t = A t + A t^2 \tan s$

$A \tan s \cdot t^2 + (A+1) t - \tan s = 0$

$$t^2 + \frac{A+1}{A \tan s} \cdot t - \frac{1}{A} = 0 \qquad \text{which by logs reduces to}$$

$$t^2 + 1 \cdot 190\, t - \cdot 522 = 0 \qquad \text{and solution of this quadratic gives}$$

$$t = \cdot 3445 = \tan \frac{a}{2}$$

from which $\underline{a = 38°.}$ (four figure accuracy).

55. LEGENDRE'S THEOREM.

This is much used when carrying out a hydrographic or ordnance survey.

All triangles measured on the surface of the earth during the course of a survey are spherical triangles and consequently the sum of the three angles in such a triangle will exceed 180°. In a survey by triangulation the largest triangles practicable are still very small indeed compared with the earth's surface and their spherical excess does not as a rule amount to more than a few seconds of arc. It requires a triangle of about 65 square nautical miles in area to produce 1 second of excess.

In only a few of the largest triangles in the Ordnance Survey of Great Britain is the spherical excess more than 30 seconds; usually it is much less.

Legendre's Theorem is of great assistance to surveyors, since in effect it reduces these spherical triangles to plane triangles. They may then be solved by the ordinary formulae of plane trigonometry.

It states as follows:—

Legendre's Theorem:—*If the sides of a spherical triangle are small compared with the radius of the sphere, then each angle of the spherical triangle exceeds by one-third of the spherical excess the corresponding angle in the plane triangle whose sides are of the same lengths as the sides of the spherical triangle.*

Proof:

It is shown in more advanced works on algebra that, if θ is in radians, then

$$\sin \theta = \theta - \frac{\theta^3}{3!} + \frac{\theta^5}{5!} - \quad \text{and}$$

$$\cos \theta = 1 - \frac{\theta^2}{2!} + \frac{\theta^4}{4!} -$$

Let A, B, C be the angles of the spherical triangle, and a, b, c its sides, all in radians; let r be the radius of the sphere; x, y, z the lengths of the arcs which form the sides, respectively.

So, for instance, $x = r\,a$, that is, $\dfrac{x}{r}$, $\dfrac{y}{r}$, $\dfrac{z}{r}$ may be written instead of a, b, c respectively.

Hence $\sin a = \dfrac{x}{r} - \dfrac{x^3}{6r^3} +$ and

$$\cos a = 1 - \frac{x^2}{2r^2} + \frac{x^4}{24r^4} -$$

Similar expressions hold good for $\cos b$, $\sin b$, $\cos c$ and $\sin c$.
Now, from the fundamental cosine formula,

$$\cos A = \frac{\cos a - \cos b \cos c}{\sin b \sin c}\ ,\ \text{and by substituting}$$

and neglecting all powers above the fourth, we have

$$\cos A = \frac{1 - \dfrac{x^2}{2r^2} + \dfrac{x^4}{24r^4} - \left(1 - \dfrac{y^2}{2r^2} + \dfrac{y^4}{24r^4}\right)\left(1 - \dfrac{z^2}{r^2} + \dfrac{z^4}{24r^4}\right)}{\dfrac{yz}{r^2}\left(1 - \dfrac{y^2}{6r^2}\right)\left(1 - \dfrac{z^2}{6r^2}\right)}$$

Multiplying up and neglecting all powers above the fourth,

$$= \frac{\dfrac{1}{2r^2}\left(y^2 + z^2 - x^2\right) + \dfrac{1}{24r^4}\left(x^4 - y^4 - z^4 - 6y^2\,z^2\right)}{\dfrac{yz}{r^2}\left(1 - \dfrac{y^2 + z^2}{6r^2}\right)}$$

and since y and z are very small and so $y^2 + z^2$ is very small indeed compared with r^2, this becomes

$$= \frac{1}{2yz}\left\{y^2 + z^2 - x^2 + \frac{1}{12r^2}\left(x^4 - y^4 - z^4 - 6y^2\,z^2\right)\right\}\left\{1 + \frac{y^2 + z^2}{6r^2}\right\}$$

and again multiplying up and neglecting powers above the fourth,

$$= \frac{y^2 + z^2 - x^2}{2yz} + \frac{x^4 + y^4 + z^4 - 2y^2\,z^2 - 2z^2\,x^2 - 2x^2\,y^2}{24yzr^2} \quad \dots \quad (1)$$

Now let A', B', C' be the angles of the plane triangle whose sides are x, y, z respectively.

Then $\cos A' = \dfrac{y^2 + z^2 - x^2}{2yz}$ ....   from $A.12$

and $x^4 + y^4 + z^4 - 2y^2\,z^2 - 2z^2\,x^2 - 2x^2\,y^2 = -4y^2\,z^2 \sin^2 A'$ from $A.14$
So substituting in (1), we have

$$\cos A = \cos A' - \frac{yz \sin^2 A'}{6r^2} \quad \dots \quad \dots \quad \dots \quad (2)$$

Now let $A = A' + \alpha$, where α is very small.

Then $\cos A = \cos (A' + \alpha) = \cos A' - \alpha \sin A'$ approx. .... (3)
and therefore from (2) and (3)

$$\alpha \sin A' = \frac{yz \sin^2 A'}{6r^2}$$

$$\alpha = \frac{yz \sin A'}{6r^2} \text{ and, if } S' = \text{area of plane triangle,}$$

we have $S' = \frac{1}{2} yz \sin A'$, so that

$$\alpha = \frac{S'}{3r^2}, \text{ that is} \qquad A = A' + \frac{S'}{3r^2} \qquad .... \qquad .... \qquad (4a)$$

Similarly, $\qquad B = B' + \frac{S'}{3r^2} \qquad .... \qquad .... \qquad (4b)$

and $\qquad C = C' + \frac{S'}{3r^2} \qquad .... \qquad .... \qquad (4c)$

Adding,

$$A + B + C = A' + B' + C' + \frac{S'}{r^2} \text{ to the degree of approximation}$$

adopted throughout. Thus $\frac{S'}{r^2}$ must be approximately equal to E,

the spherical excess and so from 4 (a), (b) and (c), **each angle of the spherical triangle exceeds the corresponding angle of the plane triangle by one-third of the spherical excess, thus proving Legendre's Theorem.**

Since in practice it is the spherical angles that are measured, it is only necessary to reduce their sum to 180° by deducting one-third of the spherical excess from each. The triangle may then be solved in terms of the lengths (linear units) of its sides by the ordinary rules of plane trigonometry.

56. APPLICATION OF LEGENDRE'S THEOREM.

There are several ways in which spherical excess may be calculated. One which is commonly employed is by use of the formula $A = E\,r^2$, as derived in para. **37**, that is

$$E = \frac{A}{r^2}$$

If A is the area of the spherical triangle in sq. nautical miles, r the mean radius of curvature of the earth's surface at that point in nautical miles, then E will be the spherical excess in radians, from which E in seconds of arc is easily derived.

G

This fact is made use of in standard works on surveying. For instance, the Admiralty Manual of Hydrographic Surveying gives a table of spherical excess against areas. From it, for example, a triangle of area 90 sq. nautical miles has an excess of 1·4 seconds of arc, one of 300 sq. nautical miles an excess of 4·6 seconds of arc, and so on.

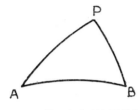

Let us take as an example, the triangle PAB, in which AB is a base line and in which the angles, measured in the course of a survey are,

$P = 38° \ 12' \ 22'' \cdot 0$

$A = 59° \ 48' \ 48'' \cdot 5$

$B = 81° \ 58' \ 50'' \cdot 7$, the area of the triangle being 80 sq. nautical miles.

The spherical excess is $1'' \cdot 2$, and deducting $0'' \cdot 4$ from each, we have

$P = 38° \ 12' \ 21'' \cdot 6$

$A = 59° \ 48' \ 48'' \cdot 1$

$B = 81° \ 58' \ 50'' \cdot 3$, and these are the angles of the plane triangle PAB, which may now be solved by the methods of plane trigonometry, obtaining the lengths of its sides (in feet.)

CHAPTER VII

NOTES ON METHODS OF SIGHT REDUCTION

57. For a century or more, navigators have been intrigued by the problem of solving the traditional *PZX* triangle by the most economical means.

In some cases advantage is taken of the special position of the heavenly body, as for example, in the case of Pole Star Tables or Ex-Meridian Tables. As a discussion of these is more appropriate to a manual on navigation, they will not be dealt with here.

There are those methods which attempt to shorten the work by various adaptations of the basic spherical formulae, sometimes with conspicuous success, as for example, in the case of the *A*, *B* and *C* Tables.

Again, there are the 'short method tables', in which the *PZX* triangle is subdivided by dropping a perpendicular from one of the angular points on to the opposite side.

Lastly, there are the fully tabular methods, which are simply tabulated solutions of the *PZX* triangle for all combinations of the arguments hour angle, latitude and declination.

We shall confine our attention in this chapter to the mathematical principles underlying the construction of such tables and only to a very minor extent to the navigational applications which are more appropriate to a manual on navigation.

It is regretted that owing to the prohibitive amount of space that would have been required, much of it with tedious repetition of tabular forms, it has not been found possible to include reproductions from the various tables named.

The student is strongly advised to study these tabular forms by reference to the volumes themselves, copies of which are available in most nautical libraries.

58. A, B AND C TABLES.

These well known tables have been in use for more than a hundred years. Although they have several applications, they are primarily regarded as a quick method of obtaining the azimuth when Azimuth Tables such as those of Burdwood or Davis are not available, and it is from this point of view that we shall consider them, since many short methods make use of them.

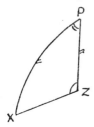

In the conventional PZX triangle, in which

PX=polar distance

$\angle P$=hour angle

PZ=co-lat.

$\angle Z$=azimuth,

then by the four-part formula,

$$\cot PX \sin PZ - \cot Z \sin P = \cos P \cos PZ,$$

and by transposing,

$$\cot PX \sin PZ - \cos P \cos PZ = \cot Z \sin P.$$

In order to make the terms in this equation (polar distance, co-lat) conform with those of the arguments which are more convenient in use (declination, latitude), both Norie and Burton divide through by $\sin P \sin PZ$, whence

$$\frac{\cot PX}{\sin P} - \cot P \cot PZ = \frac{\cot Z}{\sin PZ}$$

i.e.

tan decl. cosec hour angle — cot hour angle tan lat
B   A
=cot az. sec lat
C

In practice, Table C is entered with the algebraic sum of A and B, i.e. C, and the latitude, as arguments. Thus, in Table C,

$$(A \pm B) \cos \text{lat.} = \cot \text{az.}$$

The tables are extremely simple to use, as the following example will show.

Given Lat. 56° N., Decl. 15° N., H.A. 36° W.,

With H.A. and lat., $A = 2 \cdot 04$ S.

With H.A. and decl., $B = \cdot 46$ N.

$$C = 1 \cdot 58 \text{ S.}$$

With $C = 1 \cdot 58$ and lat., azimuth=S. 48°·5 W.

59. Methods based on direct solution of the PZX triangle.

One might describe these as solutions of the PZX triangle by direct application of the formulae of spherical trigonometry, modified to facilitate logarithmic computation. They are not really 'short' methods—not in the sense in which the term is commonly employed.

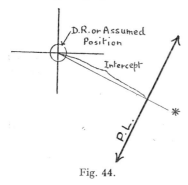

Fig. 44.

In order to plot a position line derived from an astronomical observation, it is necessary to know three things:—

(a) the D.R. Position*, or the "Assumed" or "Chosen" Position, with which the sight was worked.

(b) the azimuth of the body

(c) the intercept.

There are methods which utilise the D.R. position. This has the advantage that the results are plotted easily (since several near-simultaneous sights may all be plotted from the same D.R.). Also the intercepts are usually short and results very accurate.

However, the work of calculating the position line is considerably greater than in some of the methods we shall deal with later in this chapter.

Others employ a Special, or Assumed position, so chosen that the latitude is a whole number of degrees and the longitude is such that it makes the local hour angle a whole number of degrees. Thus more quantities can be tabulated against arguments which are hour angles and latitudes to whole degrees, interpolation is reduced, tables are more compact and labour is reduced.

However, intercepts are liable to be large. Moreover, in plotting (say) a three star fix, whilst all would be plotted from the same Assumed Latitude, the Assumed Longitudes used for each could have a spread over as much as 30' of arc, either side of the D.R.

The methods we shall now consider might all be described as 'direct methods', to distinguish them from methods which employ some degree of tabulation.

60.   DIRECT METHODS.

(a) Davis's Cosine-Haversine method.
(First proposed by Goodwin, but promoted by Davis through publication of his tables in 1914.)
This is by far the one most widely used in British ships. The following are included for their historical or international interest.

---

*Some would prefer to call this the Estimated Position, which is what it really is. However, we shall refer to it in this chapter as the D.R. position as we believe this is more in accordance with practice at sea and in the air.

(b) Aquino's Log and Versine method.

(c) Yonemura's method.

(d) Supplementary haversine method.

(e) Martelli's method.

As already stated, we shall be primarily concerned with the mathematical background and only to a limited extent with the navigational applications.

(a) **Cosine-Haversine (or Davis) method.**

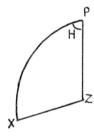

It is shown in para. 17 that, by the natural haversine formula,

hav ZX =hav $(PX{\sim}PZ)$+sin PZ sin PX hav P

Since PZ=90°−lat., sin PZ=cos lat.

and PX=90°±dec., sin PX=cos dec.

Also $PX{\sim}PZ$=(90°±dec.)${\sim}$(90°−lat.)

that is

hav $(PX{\sim}PZ)$=hav (lat.${\sim}$dec.) since for any combination of signs the 90° terms cancel out.

Hence the nat. haversine formula becomes, writing H (hour angle) instead of P,

hav ZX =hav (lat${\sim}$dec.) +cos lat. cos dec. hav H (1)

This is the Cosine-Haversine formula. For many navigators at sea it still remains the standard method of sight reduction.

As explained in para. 17, equation (1) may be written

hav ZX =hav (lat${\sim}$dec)+hav θ   ....   (2)

where the parameter θ is some angle such that

hav θ =cos lat. cos dec. hav H ....   (2.a)

In nautical tables such as Inman's, Norie's or Burton's, natural and logarithmic haversines are tabulated side by side, an arrangement which simplifies the work of sight reduction.

(b) **Aquino**, in his Log and Versine tables, doubles equation (2)

Thus, vers ZX =vers (lat.${\sim}$dec.)+vers θ   ....   (3)

where vers θ=2 $\sin^2 \dfrac{θ}{2}$ =2 cos lat cos dec $\sin^2 \dfrac{H}{2}$ (from 2.a)

Thus, in logarithmic form, and using reciprocals,

log cosec $\dfrac{θ}{2}$ =½ log sec lat+½ log sec dec+log cosec $\dfrac{H}{2}$ (4)

Aquino gives a table of $\frac{1}{2}$ log secants for every minute of arc, together with tables of natural versines of the argument side by side with log cosecants of half the argument.

It is easy to see that with the sum of the three quantities on the R.H.S. of equation (4) as argument in the log cosec $\dfrac{\theta}{2}$ column, vers θ may be taken out. This, added to vers (lat⌢dec) in equation (3) will give vers ZX.

In both the Davis and Aquino methods separate provision must be made for finding the azimuth.

Davis obtains it by his Azimuth Tables, giving azimuths to $0°\cdot1$ usually for every degree of latitude declination and hour angle.

Using Inman's tables one must refer to Davis's azimuth tables, whilst Norie and Burton provide azimuths by means of the A, B and C Tables already described (para. 58).

(c) **Yonemura** uses the same parameter θ, but expressed in reciprocal form, that is, from (2.a),

$$\frac{1}{\text{hav } \theta} = \text{sec lat. sec dec.} \frac{1}{\text{hav } H} \qquad \text{....} \qquad \text{.... and from (1)}$$

$$\frac{1}{\text{hav } ZX} = \frac{1}{\text{hav (lat⌢dec)}} + \text{sec lat. sec dec.} \frac{1}{\text{hav } H} \quad \text{....} \qquad (5)$$

This is Yonemura's formula. His tables include natural and logarithmic values of the reciprocals of the haversines, as well as log secants. Except for this difference in the tabulated values, the sight is reduced on the same lines as the Davis and Aquino methods.

He does however also include means of finding the azimuth, using the sine formula. Thus, in the triangle PZX,

$$\frac{\sin \text{ az.}}{\sin PX} = \frac{\sin H}{\sin ZX}$$

i.e. $\sin$ az.$=\sin H \cos$ dec. sec alt.   ....   (6)

A disadvantage of this formula is that the result may be ambiguous, as in all cases when an angle is found through its sine (para. 20).

(d) **Supplementary Haversine method.**

This method used a function which has been termed the supplementary haversine of x, or shav x.

This function is defined as $\frac{1}{2}(1+\cos x)$ which equals $(1-\text{hav } x)$.

Also $\frac{1}{2}(1+\cos x) = \frac{1}{2}[1-\cos(180°-x)]$

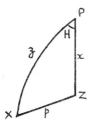

$$=\text{hav }(180°-x)$$

$$=\text{shav } x$$

In the triangle PZX, by the fundamental formula, $\cos p = \cos x \cos z + \sin x \sin z \cos H$, which may be written,

$$\cos p = \cos x \cos z \left(\cos^2 \frac{H}{2} + \sin^2 \frac{H}{2}\right) + \sin x \sin z \left(\cos^2 \frac{H}{2} - \sin^2 \frac{H}{2}\right)$$

$$=\cos(x\sim z)\cos^2 \frac{H}{2} + \cos(x+z)\sin^2 \frac{H}{2} \qquad \text{....} \qquad \text{....} \qquad \text{(i)}$$

But by their definitions,

$$\text{hav } H = \frac{1}{2}(1-\cos H) = \sin^2 \frac{H}{2}$$

and $\text{shav } H = \frac{1}{2}(1+\cos H) = \cos^2 \frac{H}{2}$ and so by substituting in (1)

$$1-2\text{ hav } p = \left\{1 - 2\text{ hav }(x\sim z)\right\}\cos^2 \frac{H}{2} + \left\{1 - 2\text{ hav }(x+z)\right\}\sin^2 \frac{H}{2}$$

whence

$$\text{hav } p = \text{hav }(x\sim z)\text{ shav } H + \text{hav }(x+z)\text{ hav } H \qquad \text{....} \qquad \text{(ii)}$$

In this, it will be seen that

$$x\sim z = (90°-\text{lat.})\sim(90°\pm \text{dec.}) = \text{lat.}\sim\text{dec.}$$

Also

$$x+z = (90°-\text{lat.})+(90°\pm\text{dec.}) = 180°-(\text{lat.}+\text{dec.}),$$

latitude and declination being given their correct signs throughout.

Formula (ii) now becomes

$$\text{hav } ZX = \text{hav }(\text{lat}\sim\text{dec.})\text{ shav } H + \text{shav }(\text{lat.}+\text{dec.})\text{hav } H \qquad (7)$$

This is the formula used for calculating zenith distance.

It may also be written

$$\text{hav } ZX = \text{hav } \alpha + \text{hav } \beta \qquad \text{....} \qquad \text{....} \qquad \text{....} \qquad \text{....} \qquad (7.a)$$

in which α and β are parameters in the same sense as θ (formula $(2.a)$)

Thus it can be evaluated as it stands by ordinary haversine tables.

However it is possible to arrange the tables so that hav α and vha β can be looked up directly with the hour angle (H) and lat.$\sim$ dec. and lat.+dec. as arguments, though working from a D.R. position would make such tables rather bulky.

If however the sight is worked from an Assumed Position so as to make the hour angle and the latitude a whole number of degrees, the number of entries is reduced to three, the tables are concise and the method could be regarded as amongst the best of the short tabular methods.

In spite of this, it never seems to have been widely used.

A further development of formula (i) can make it yield azimuths but the method is not very convenient and most navigators would prefer azimuth or A B C tables.

(e) Martelli's method.

These tables designed by Martelli in 1873 are derived from the cosine-haversine formula. When worked with the D.R. latitude, they give the longitude in which the position line intersects the D.R. latitude. This distinguishes them sharply from methods (a) to (d), which all give intercept on the Marq St. Hilaire principle.

By the cosine-haversine formula, putting $ZX=z$, lat.$=l$, decl.$=d$, hour angle$=H$, we have

$$\text{hav } z = \text{hav } (l\sim d) + \cos l \cos d \text{ hav } H$$

$$\text{hav } H = \frac{\text{hav } z - \text{hav } (l\sim d)}{\cos l \cos d} \text{ , whence}$$

$$\frac{10\cdot8}{\text{hav } H} = \sqrt{10 \cos l} \sqrt{10 \cos d} \times \frac{1\cdot08}{\text{hav } z - \text{hav } (l\sim d)} \text{ ....} \qquad (8)$$

This is the formula used by Martelli in compiling his tables.

The procedure seems a little involved at first, (there are five separate tables), but arithmetic is kept to a minimum by the use of four-figure computations, with some consequent loss in accuracy.

The tables also provide means of obtaining the azimuth from the formula

sin az.$=$sin H cos dec. sec alt.   ....   (9)

As in the Yonemura method, the formula is ambiguous.

61. TABULAR METHODS.

These might be said to be the opposite extreme from the methods we have just been considering. They are virtually complete solutions of the PZX triangle already worked out for all combinations of latitude, declination and hour angle to 1° intervals.

Thus, they are best used from a "chosen" or "assumed" position, that is one in which the latitude is a whole number of degrees, and the longitude is chosen so as to make the hour angle a whole number of degrees.

By direct entry with the three arguments (lat., dec., hour angle) the zenith distance and azimuth are extracted.

The three best-known are

(a) **Tables of Computed Altitudes and Azimuths.**

> (Published in the U.K. as H.D. 486 and in the U.S.A. as H.O. 214, six volumes.)

(b) **Sight Reduction Tables for Marine Navigation.**

> (Published in the U.K. as N.P. 401 and in the U.S.A. as H.O. 229, six volumes. These are very similar to, and seem likely to replace, (a).)

(c) **Sight Reduction Tables for Air Navigation.**

> (Published in the U.K. as A.P. 3270 and in the U.S.A. as H.O. 249, three volumes. An interesting feature is that Vol. 1 gives tables for seven 'selected stars', enabling altitude and azimuth to be extracted by a single entry.
>
> For this reason they have gained popularity among mariners.)

The mathematical background to these tables calls for no comment. As already stated, the tables simply consist of calculated solutions of the PZX triangle for $1°$ intervals of the arguments.

In use, they undoubtedly provide the quickest method of sight reduction. There are disadvantages in respect to bulk (each consisting of a series of substantial volumes to cover all bands of latitude) and price. Intercepts may be fairly large, and a slight complication in plotting results from the fact that each sight is worked with a different assumed longitude.

Even so, three or four stars can be reduced and plotted on the chart within the space of some ten minutes, which is not possible by any other method. If speed were the only criterion, they would be the only method used.

They provide the standard method of sight reduction in the Royal Navy and Royal Air Force, but the Merchant fleets of the world have been slow to adopt them.

62. METHODS USING AN ASSUMED OR CHOSEN POSITION.

These might be termed "mixed" methods, in the sense that they involve some degree of tabulation, falling short, however, of the fully tabular methods mentioned in para. 61.

They all fall in the category of what is commonly implied by the term "Short Methods". The principle employed is the same throughout, namely, to subdivide the PZX triangle by a perpendicular dropped from one of the angles on to the opposite side. The resulting right angled triangles may then be solved by the use of Napier's Rules.

Examples (named after their authors, except Hughes, who is the publisher) are given below:—

(a) **Perpendicular from Z on to PX.**

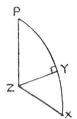

Ogura.   (A and K).
Dreisonstok.
Hughes' Tables.
Gingrich.
Smart and Shearme (or Sine method)
Myerscough and Hamilton.
Lieuwen.
Aquino (Tabular).

(b) **Perpendicular from X on to PZ.**

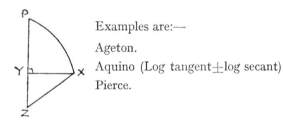

Examples are:—

Ageton.

Aquino (Log tangent±log secant)

Pierce.

Although some of these are now only of historical interest, they have been included because of the important part they have played in the development of the subject.

As it is sometimes necessary to compare one method with another, the following broad principles should be noted:—

If the perpendicular is dropped from Z on to PX, it is easier to work with a latitude which is a whole number of degrees, but a disadvantage is that the azimuth angle is in two parts.

The converse is the case when the perpendicular is dropped from X on to PZ.

The reader should keep these in mind as they will not be referred to again in the text. In the discussions which now follow, we shall confine ourselves to any special features of a particular method.

63. OGURA (A AND K TABLES).

First published in Tokyo in 1920, with an English edition in 1924, these are amongst the earliest of the genuinely "short method" tables. They are still included in Norie's Nautical Tables and moreover, many tables since then have been based on the principles used by Ogura.

In them, the spherical triangle PZX is divided by a perpendicular from Z on to PX.

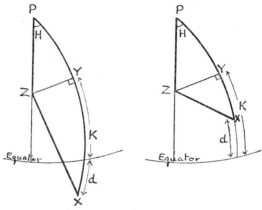

Fig. 45. Ogura Method

The figure illustrates the principle used. It will be observed that the quantity K given in the tables is the declination of the point Y. We shall see shortly that the quantity A in the tables is really the log secant of ZY.

With the usual notation, in triangle PZY, sometimes called the **time triangle**, we have, by Napier's Rules,

$$\cos H = \cot PZ \tan PY$$
$$\tan PY = \cos H \tan PZ$$

i.e. $\qquad \mathbf{cot}\ K = \mathbf{cos}\ H\ \mathbf{cot\ lat}..$ $\qquad$ .. $\qquad$ .. $\qquad$ **(1)**

Also, $\quad \sin ZY = \sin H \sin PZ$

i.e. $\qquad \mathbf{sin}\ ZY = \mathbf{sin}\ H\ \mathbf{cos\ lat}$ $\qquad$ .. $\qquad$ .. $\qquad$ **(2)**

In triangle ZYX, sometimes called the **altitude triangle**, in which $YX = K \sim d$, we have

$$\cos ZX = \cos ZY \cos YX$$
$$\sin \text{alt.} = \cos ZY \cos (K \sim d) \qquad \text{and turning each into its}$$
$$\text{reciprocal,}$$

$\qquad \mathbf{cosec\ alt.} = \mathbf{sec}\ ZY\ \mathbf{sec}\ (K \sim d) \qquad$ .. $\qquad$ **(3)**

quantities which are all greater than unity and therefore a little easier to deal with than sines and cosines.

It should be noted that:—

(i) As long as the hour angle is less than 6 hours E. or W. of the meridian the quantity $K + d$ can never be greater than $90°$. This makes for some simplification in use.

(ii) In addition to the A and K tables, log secants (for $K{\sim}d$) and log cosecants (to obtain calculated altitude) are required—or one may dispense with the log cosecants and use the secant of its complement.

(iii) The tables as printed in early editions of *Norie* do not provide azimuths. Later editions do so.

64. DREISONSTOK TABLES. (First published 1929).

These have a great deal in common with the Ogura Tables just described.

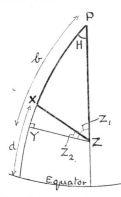

Again the perpendicular is dropped from Z on to PX (produced if necessary.) Instead of the quantity K, however, which is the declination of Y, the foot of the perpendicular from Z, Dreisonstok works with b, the complement of K. This leads to the slight complication that $b+d$ can exceed 90°, even for hour angles less than 6 hours.

Fig. 46. Dreisonstok method.

The equations are as follows:—

In triangle PZY,
$$\cos H = \cot PZ \tan PY$$
i.e.   **$\tan b = \cos H \cot \text{lat}$** .. .. .. **(1)**

Also, $\sin ZY = \sin H \sin PZ$
i.e.   **$\sin ZY = \sin H \cos \text{lat}$** .. .. **(2)**

In triangle ZYX, $XY = 90° {\sim} (b{\sim}d)$, and
$$\cos ZX = \cos ZY \cos XY$$
$$\sin \text{alt.} = \cos ZY \sin (b{\sim}d)$$
i.e.   **$\text{cosec alt.} = \sec ZY \text{ cosec } (b{\sim}d)$** .. **(3)**

It will be seen that these three equations bear a striking similarity to the corresponding equations used by Ogura.

In addition however, the tables do give azimuths, the equations being:—

In triangle PZY,
$$\cos PZ = \cot H \cot Z_1$$
i.e.   **$\tan Z_1 = \cot H \text{ cosec lat}$** .. **(4)**

and in triangle ZYX, in which $XY = 90° - (b \sim d)$

$$\sin ZY = \tan XY \cot Z_2$$

i.e. $\tan Z_2 = \cot (b \sim d) \operatorname{cosec} ZY$ ..   **(5)**

Clearly, from equations (4) and (5) in this case,

$$Z_1 - Z_2 = \text{azimuth.}$$

In other cases, in accordance with rules given in the tables, the sum $Z_1 + Z_2$ must be taken in order to obtain the azimuth.

In conclusion, therefore, regarding Dreisonstok's Tables, it will be observed that:—

(i) There is the slight complication, already referred to, that $b + d$ frequently exceeds 90°.

(ii) The tables are complete in themselves, including all necessary log cosecants and cotangents.

(iii) The azimuth is found as the sum or difference of the two angles at Z.

65. HUGHES' TABLES FOR SEA AND AIR NAVIGATION.

(First published 1938).

These tables were prepared with encouragement from the British Admiralty and were published by Henry Hughes and Sons. They were based extensively on the work of Ogura and Dreisonstok in an effort to combine the best features of both, in which, on the whole, they were successful.

The sight is worked from an assumed position giving latitude and hour angle to a whole degree.

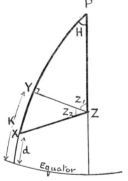

The PZX triangle is divided by a perpendicular from Z on to PX, and the K and d of Ogura are used as well as the Z_1 and Z_2 of Dreisonstok.

Fig. 47   Hughes Method

The relevant equations are:—

After Ogura, for altitude,

$$\cot K = \cos H \cot \text{lat} \quad .. \qquad .. \qquad .. \qquad \textbf{(1)}$$

$$\sin ZY = \sin H \cos \text{lat} \quad .. \qquad .. \qquad .. \qquad \textbf{(2)}$$

$$\textbf{cosec alt} = \textbf{sec}\, ZY\, \textbf{sec}\, (K \sim d) \quad .. \qquad .. \qquad \textbf{(3)}$$

After Dreisonstok, for azimuth

$$\tan Z_1 = \textbf{cot}\, H\, \textbf{cosec lat} \qquad .. \qquad .. \qquad \textbf{(4)}$$

$$\tan Z_2 = \tan(K \sim d)\, \textbf{cosec}\, ZY \, .. \qquad .. \qquad \textbf{(5)}$$

It should be noted that the tables are arranged with latitude at the top of the page. This is a great improvement, since if three or four bodies are observed they would all normally be worked with the same chosen latitude and their hour angles will all be on one page.

These were excellent tables, containing everything within one volume. However, they have now very largely been superceded by H.D. 486. (See para. 61).

66. GINGRICH—AERIAL AND MARINE NAVIGATION TABLES.

These were first published in New York in 1931, so chronologically they come after Dreisonstok and before Hughes. They are a good re-arrangement and were extensively used before, unfortunately, they went out of print.

The PZX triangle is divided by a perpendicular from Z on to PX, and the A and K used by Gingrich are the same as those of Ogura.

The method of obtaining the azimuth however, is different from its predecessors, his X and Y being the A and B of Norie and Burton, as developed from the four-part formula (see para. 58). On the whole this is simpler than the Z_1 and Z_2 of Dreisonstok.

TABLE A

Lat. Dec.	H.A. 30°			
	A	K	X	Y
	—	—	—	—
	—	—	—	—
40°	—	—	—	—

Fig. 48. Outline of Gingrich Tables

Thus, entering Table A with the arguments hour angle and latitude, one extracts A, K and X, and on the same page, against the declination, Y.

($K{\sim}d$) is the same as for Ogura, and the altitude is obtained in the same way, a Table B being provided which is simply a table of log secants and log cosecants.

X and Y are combined algebraically and with the result, the azimuth may be extracted from the Azimuth Table which is also included.

Thus, the volume is complete in itself and on the whole, especially in the method of obtaining the azimuth, represents an advance on what had gone before.

67. SMART AND SHEARME TABLES, OR SINE METHOD.

These tables were based on some earlier work published by Smart in 1919 and were published in London as "Position Line Tables (Sine Method)" in 1922. They are included in Inman's Nautical Tables.

Although developed independently and several years earlier, these tables closely resemble Dreisonstok in that they use a quantity U, which is exactly the same as Dreisonstok's b, the polar distance of the foot of the perpendicular from Z on to $P\overline{X}$. The other quantity tabulated is V, which is the log cosine of ZY.

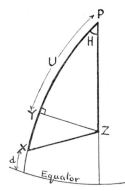

The arguments used are the latitude, to the chosen whole degree at the top of the page, and the hour angle down the side at intervals of 4 minutes of time, which complicates slightly the choosing of the special longitude with which the sight must be worked.

Fig. 49. Smart and Shearme method.

The equations, which may be compared with the derivation of those used by Dreisonstok, in para. 64, are as follows:—

$$\tan U = \cos H \cot \text{lat} \quad \ldots \qquad \ldots \qquad \ldots \qquad (1)$$

$$\sin ZY = \sin H \cos \text{lat} \quad \ldots \qquad \ldots \qquad \ldots \qquad (2)$$

$$\sin \text{alt.} = \cos ZY \sin (U \sim d) \quad \ldots \qquad \ldots \qquad (3)$$

(Dreisonstok used (3) in its reciprocal form of secants and cosecants, which undoubtedly simplified the logarithmic work.)

As used by Smart and Shearme, (3) becomes

log sin alt$=V+$log sin $(U{\sim}d)$, where V is log cos ZY, a form which gave rise to its sub-title, the "Sine Method".

As given in Inman's, the tables make no provision for obtaining the azimuth, nor do they include the necessary tables of log sines, as required in (3).

68. RAPID NAVIGATION TABLES (MYERSCOUGH AND HAMILTON).

These were published in London in 1939. They are therefore amongst the most recent of the attempts down the years to evolve the 'perfect' short method. They are still in general use and we propose to consider them in rather more detail.

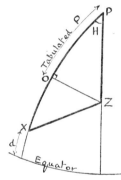

Once again the PZX triangle is divided by a perpendicular from Z on to PX.

For altitude, the tabulated quantity P is the polar distance of the foot of the perpendicular (i.e. Dreisonstok's b) and PO in the figure.

For azimuth, X and Y, as in Gingrich or the A and B tables, are combined to give Z, i.e. Norie's or Burton's C.

Fig. 50. Myerscough and Hamilton method.

The equations are as follows:—

By Napier's Rules, in triangle ZPO,

$$\tan PO =\cos H \tan PZ \qquad \qquad \qquad (1)$$

and $\quad\sin ZO =\sin H \sin PZ \qquad \qquad \qquad (2)$

(See Dreisonstok, (1) and (2), para. 66.)

Again, in triangle ZOX,

$$\cos ZX =\cos ZO \cos XO \qquad \qquad \qquad (3)$$

and inverting,

sec $ZX=$sec ZO sec XO

H

that is,

$$\sec \text{ zenith dist.} = \sec ZO \sec (PO \sim PX)$$

$$= \sec ZO \sec [PO \sim (90 \pm \text{decl.})]$$

i.e.   **cosec alt.** $= \sec ZO$ **cosec** $(PO + \text{decl.})^*$ **(4)**

*Add if same names, and conversely.

H.A. 41°

Lat° Alt'	P	Q	R	X	Y	Az.	Z
0	—	—	—	—	—	—	—
1	—	—	—	—	—	—	with X±Y
2	—	—	— —	—	—	Az. ↲	

Fig. 51. Outline of Myerscough and Hamilton Tables.

In the tables, entering with hour angle and latitude, each to the nearest whole degree, one extracts

> P, the value of PO in degrees and minutes of arc, which must be combined with the declination, in accordance with the rules, to obtain $(P \pm \text{decl.})$. Note that the rules are printed on every page.

> Q, the value of log secant ZO ($\times 10^5$ to remove decimal point.)

> R, the value of log cosecant $(P \pm \text{decl.})$ ($\times 10^5$ to remove decimal point.)

Example 1. Given hour angle 96°, latitude 40° N., decl. 19° 22' S., calculate the values of P and Q as given in M. and H. Tables.

From (1.) tan PO=cos 96° tan 50° |9·01924
    and PO=7° 06'   ·07619
    i.e. P=7° 06' S.
                                 |9·09543

From (2.) sin ZO=sin 96° sin 50° |9·99761
    ZO=49° 37'·6   9·88425
and log sec $ZO \times 10^5$=18858=Q
                                 |9·88186

Using this data, show how to compute the calculated altitude.

Using equation (4.)

$$P \qquad 7° 06' \text{ S.}$$
$$\text{Decl.} \quad 19° 22' \text{ S.}$$

$P+$Decl. 26° 28'   and cosec$=35098$ (i.e. R)

$\qquad\qquad\qquad\qquad\qquad\qquad$ 18858   (Q)

$\qquad\qquad\qquad\qquad Q+R$ 53956

and again in the table of cosecants, calculated altitude$=16° 46'\cdot7$

An advantage of M. and H. Tables over many others is that they also provide the azimuth.

The method used is identical with the A, B and C Tables already described (para. 58). The quantities tabulated are X, Y and Z.

From the four-part formula, it was shown in para. 58 that cot az. sec lat.$=$tan decl. cosec hour angle$-$tan lat. cot hour angle i.e.

cot $\angle PZX$ cosec PZ

(Z)

$=$ **cot PX cosec $\angle ZPX-$cot PZ cot $\angle ZPX$**

(Y) $\qquad\qquad\qquad$ **(X)**

In the tables

$\qquad$ column X gives cot PZ cot $\angle ZPX \times 10$

$\qquad\qquad$,, $\quad Y \quad$,, $\quad$ cot PX cosec $\angle ZPX \times 10$

$\qquad\qquad$,, $\quad Z \quad$,, $\quad$ cot $\angle PZX$ cosec $PZ \times 10$

As in the A, B and C Tables, the naming (N. or S.) of the tabulated values of X and Y is so arranged that one always takes the algebraic sum (i.e. like names add, unlike names subtract) and entering table Z with $X\pm Y$, the azimuth may be extracted at sight.

These tables are very convenient to use. All the requisite data is available (intercept and azimuth) in one volume, and with the minimum number of entries. All pages have a uniform appearance and as already stated, the rules for using the tables are printed on every page.

The accuracy claimed is high, namely a maximum error of $0'\cdot5$ of arc in the calculated altitude and a maximum error of $0°\cdot25$ in the azimuth, compared with the values that could be obtained by 6-figure logarithms in the triangle PZX.

H*

69. LIEUWEN'S SHORT METHOD NAVIGATION TABLES.

Originally published in Holland by Order of the Dutch Ministry of Marine, the English edition appeared in 1951.   In his preface the author states that the Dutch edition was made *"compulsory for all schools and colleges of the Navy and Mercantile Marine"*.

Later in 1953, he expresses the view that *"nowadays the tendency to determine a fix by means of shortened methods is universally prevalent"*. If only he were right! A recent investigation among Navigating Officers in British merchant ships showed that only 27% habitually use short methods in star sight reduction.*

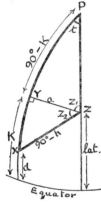

The *PZX* triangle is divided by a perpendicular from *Z* on to *PX*.

K is the declination of the foot of the perpendicular, like Ogura.

The hour angle is *t*, and altitude *h*.

Fig. 52. Lieuwen method.

In the triangle *PZY*,
$$\cot K = \cot \text{lat} \cos t \qquad (1)$$

and $\qquad \sin a = \cos \text{lat} \sin t \qquad \cdots \qquad \cdots \qquad \cdots \qquad (2)$

both of which are like Ogura's (1) and (2.)

Also (in same triangle)
$$\cot Z_1 = \sin \text{lat} \tan t \qquad \cdots \qquad \cdots \qquad \cdots \qquad (3)$$

which is Dreisonstok's (4.) in reciprocal form.

Again, in the triangle *ZYX*,
$$\csc \text{alt} = \sec a \sec (K-d) \qquad \cdots \qquad \cdots \qquad (4)$$

which is like Ogura's (3.)

Finally, for Z_2 we have,
$$\sin a = \tan (K-d) \cot Z_2 \cdots \qquad \cdots \qquad \cdots \qquad (5)$$

It will be seen that once again the azimuth is made up of two parts, Z_1 and Z_2.

---

* Journal of the Institute of Navigation, London, 1966

It is claimed for the method that the D.R. position may be used, a simplification in some respects, but on the other hand, additional small corrections must be included. These are given in the c_1 table, a "latitude correction" and in the c_2 table, a "time correction".

It must be admitted that the rules governing the use of these tables call for a great deal of care in their application.

70. LIEUWEN'S RECORD TABLES.

These were published in 1953 and the main difference between them and the earlier tables by the same author is in the arrangement, which seems to be designed to encourage working from an Assumed Position. This carries with it the disadvantages inherent in such methods, viz., large intercepts and some complication in plotting each observation from a different assumed longitude. However, there is the compensating advantage that the work is vastly shortened and these tables must be counted amongst the best of their kind. A four star fix may be worked out with only nine openings of the tables and (so it is claimed) in 10 minutes of time. This is good by any standards.

Although the arrangement of the tables is different, the same quantities, K, a, Z_1, and Z_2 are used and are calculated from precisely the same equations as in his Short Method tables.

The symbol, B, which is log sec $K \pm d$, is now tabulated by name, so that, referring to equation (4.) of previous paragraph, namely,
$$\text{cosec alt.} = \sec a \sec (K-d)$$

i.e. log cosec alt. $=\log \sec a + \log \sec (K-d)$
$$(A) \quad + \quad (B)$$

There are three tables, A, B, and A+B on each page. All pages have accordingly a uniform appearance throughout the book (see also Myerscough and Hamilton, for which the same advantage may be claimed.)

The tables also include an "approximate altitude column", so that the calculated altitude just obtained may be checked at sight and risk of arithmetical error greatly reduced.

Finally, if desired, the altitudes can be adjusted by Supplementary Tables to yield their values as if worked from a D.R. position. This additional complication seems hardly worth while.

The rules for combining and naming the various quantities are fairly complicated and would take some little time to master (see Myerscough and Hamilton where the rules are printed on every page.)

The tables are valid for all latitudes, all declinations and all hour angles—in fact it is claimed that "they are subject to no limitations whatsoever". Why is it that such "short methods" as this (and others just as good by British authors) have not "caught on" to any appreciable extent in the British Merchant fleet? We do not know—unless perhaps Lieuwen himself provides the answer in the first of his two comments, quoted in italics at the beginning of the previous paragraph!

71. AQUINO'S TABULAR METHOD.

These tables were published in Rio de Janeiro in 1943. Although they are a distinct improvement on full-length methods such as the cosine-haversine, they are still not amongst the shortest of short methods and have never been widely used by British navigators.

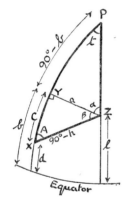

We shall consider them briefly.

Once again the *PZX* triangle is divided by a perpendicular from *Z* on to *PX*. The hour angle is given the symbol *t*, and the remaining parts are named in the diagram in accordance with the notation used by Aquino.

Fig. 53. Aquino's Tabular

The following equations may easily be deduced:—

In the time triangle, PZY,

$$\mathbf{cosec}\ a = \mathbf{cosec}\ t\ \mathbf{sec}\ l \qquad \dots \qquad \dots \qquad \dots \qquad \mathbf{(1)}$$

$$\mathbf{tan}\ b = \mathbf{sec}\ t\ \mathbf{tan}\ l \qquad \dots \qquad \dots \qquad \dots \qquad \mathbf{(2)}$$

$$\mathbf{tan}\ \alpha = \mathbf{cosec}\ l\ \mathbf{tan}\ t \qquad \dots \qquad \dots \qquad \dots \qquad \mathbf{(3)}$$

In the altitude triangle, ZYX,

$$\mathbf{cosec}\ h = \mathbf{sec}\ a\ \mathbf{sec}\ C \qquad \dots \qquad \dots \qquad \dots \qquad \mathbf{(4)}$$

$$\mathbf{tan}\ A = \mathbf{tan}\ a\ \mathbf{cosec}\ C \qquad \dots \qquad \dots \qquad \dots \qquad \mathbf{(5)}$$

$$\mathbf{tan}\ \beta = \mathbf{cosec}\ a\ \mathbf{tan}\ C \qquad \dots \qquad \dots \qquad \dots \qquad \mathbf{(6)}$$

From the first three equations, the tables give the values of a, b

and α, entering with the arguments t (in whole degrees) and latitude (to 10' intervals).

Comparison of equations (4) (5) (6) with (1) (2) (3) respectively will show that by utilising complements in some cases the same tables can be used to give h, A and β. Unfortunately however, they cannot now be entered with the exact tabulated arguments, so that a good deal of interpolation is necessary.

The sight is plotted from a Special Position which is evolved in order to round of certain of the tabulated values as the computation proceeds. Thus each sight is plotted from a different position.

The methods of combining b and d to give C, and α and β to give azimuth are governed by rather complex rules which further detract from the usefulness of the method and place it at a disadvantage compared with other short method tables.

Notwithstanding these two drawbacks, the accuracy of the tables is high and results agree closely with those obtained by direct calculation.

72. TRIANGLE DIVIDED BY A PERPENDICULAR FROM X.

This method of subdividing the PZX triangle is not so convenient if we wish to retain the advantage of working from an Assumed Position. The principal tables using this method are by:—

1. Ageton.

2. Aquino.   (Log tangent$\pm$log secant method)

3. Pierce.

These differ from most of those we have just been discussing in that they do not require an Assumed Position (in which the latitude is a whole number of degrees and the longitude makes the L.H.A. a whole number of degrees). The first two may be worked from *any* position—the D.R. would be the natural choice. The third has to be worked from a special position which must be chosen to meet the requirements of the tables.

In all three cases, therefore, there is liable to be some interpolation.

An advantage, however, is that the azimuth can be found direct, in one operation, and not as a result of the addition of two quantities as in most of the previous short methods. Also, as previously mentioned, working from a D.R. position keeps intercepts small and simplifies plotting.

73. AGETON'S METHOD.

This was devised by Lieut. A. A. Ageton of the U.S. Navy, and was first published in 1931.

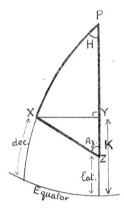

The figure illustrates the subdivision of triangle PZX.

It will be seen that the quantity K used by Ageton is the declination of the foot of the perpendicular, Y.

The sight may be worked from the D.R. or any other position.

Fig. 54. Ageton method

In the triangle PXY,

$$\sin XY = \sin PX \sin H$$
$$\sin XY = \cos \text{dec.} \sin H \text{ and in reciprocal form}$$
$$\textbf{cosec } XY = \textbf{sec dec cosec } H \qquad .. \qquad .. \qquad (1)$$

Again, $\cos PX = \cos XY \cos PY$

$$\sin \text{dec} = \cos XY \sin K$$

$$\textbf{cosec } K = \frac{\textbf{cosec dec}}{\textbf{sec } XY} \qquad .. \qquad .. \qquad .. \qquad (2)$$

The advantage of the secant—cosecant form is that negative characteristics are avoided. Decimals are avoided by multiplying all logs by 10^5. However, the tables are unreliable when K lies between 87° 30′ and 92° 30′. As one cannot know this in advance, a perfectly good sight may have to be discarded for this reason.

Also with hour angles near 90°, an error of 1′ or 2′ may occur in the computed altitude.

In the triangle XYZ,

$$\cos ZX = \cos XY \cos YZ$$
$$\sin \text{alt.} = \cos XY \cos (K \sim \text{lat}) \text{ and in reciprocal form}$$
$$\textbf{cosec alt} = \textbf{sec } XY \textbf{ sec } (K \sim \text{lat}) \quad .. \qquad .. \qquad (3)$$

Again, sin $XY = $ sin $\angle XZY$ sin ZX

$$\textbf{cosec az} = \frac{\textbf{cosec } XY}{\textbf{sec alt}} \qquad .. \qquad .. \qquad .. \qquad \textbf{(4)}$$

Ageton's tables are published by the U.S. Hydrographic Office in H.O. 211. They are simply tables of log cosecants and secants, identical with those in Table 2 (B and C) of Hughes' tables (para. 67).

All pages are identical in appearance and the method is uniform in all cases (though subject to the limitations already referred to).

74.   AQUINO'S "LOG TANGENT±LOG SECANT" METHOD.

As in the Ageton method, the perpendicular is dropped from X on to PZ.

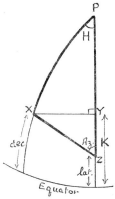

The figure illustrates the notation used in the tables, which bears a striking resemblance to that used by Ageton, although the two were developed independently. Like Ageton, the sight is worked from the D.R. position.

Fig. 55.   Aquino "log tan±log sec" method.

In the time triangle PXY, by Napier's rules,
cos $H = $ tan PY cot PX

i.e. $\textbf{tan } K = \textbf{sec } H \textbf{ tan dec}$ $\qquad .. \qquad .. \qquad .. \qquad$ **(1)**

Also, sin $PY = $ tan XY cot H

i.e. $\textbf{tan } XY = \dfrac{\textbf{tan } H}{\textbf{sec } K}$ $.. \qquad .. \qquad .. \qquad .. \qquad$ **(2)**

In the altitude triangle ZXY,
sin $ZY = $ tan XY cot az.

i.e. $\textbf{tan az} = \textbf{tan} XY \textbf{ sec } (90° - \overline{K \sim \text{lat}})$ $\qquad .. \qquad$ **(3)**

Also, $\cos az = \tan ZY \cot ZX$

$$\textbf{tan alt} = \frac{\textbf{tan } (90° - \overline{K \sim \text{lat}})}{\textbf{sec az}} \quad .. \quad .. \quad \textbf{(4)}$$

It will be observed that all the computations require only tables of log secants and log tangents. Because the tangent is used in place of the cosecant, the method is not subject to the limitations referred to in Ageton's method. The advantage is retained of obtaining the azimuth direct.

75. PIERCE METHOD.

This method originated in the United States, and is published in the U.S. Hydrographic Office publications, H.O. 209. It has not been used to any extent by British navigators.

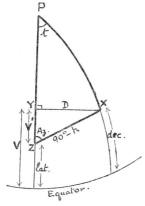

Like the Ageton method, the perpendicular is dropped from X on to PZ and the declination of the foot of the perpendicular is given the symbol V (K in Ageton). The hour angle is tabulated as t, the perpendicular, XY, is tabulated as D, and finally ($V \sim$ lat) is tabulated as V'

Fig. 56. Pierce method.

In triangle PXY,

$$\textbf{sin } D = \textbf{sin } t \textbf{ cos dec} \quad .. \quad .. \quad .. \quad \textbf{(1)}$$

and again, $\cos PX = \cos D \cos PY$

i.e. $$\textbf{sin } V = \textbf{sec } D \textbf{ sin dec} \quad .. \quad .. \quad .. \quad \textbf{(2)}$$

In triangle ZXY,

$$\textbf{sin } h = \textbf{cos } V' \textbf{cos } D \quad .. \quad .. \quad .. \quad \textbf{(3)}$$

and again, $\sin D = \sin ZX \sin az.$

i.e. $$\textbf{sin az} = \textbf{sin } D \textbf{ sec } h \quad .. \quad .. \quad .. \quad \textbf{(4)}$$

These are the equations from which the various quantities may be calculated.

The method is fairly straightforward and is subject to no limitations. The use of the declination to the nearest 6' introduces only a slight error, acceptable in most practical work. If needed, one may interpolate for the exact declination, but the increased complication is hardly worth while.

The sight is not worked with the D.R. position but with a special "Chosen Position." This is determined during the computations in order to meet the requirements of the tabulations themselves and in this respect the tables have something in common with Aquino's (Tabular) Method. Thus each sight will have a different Chosen Position, which, although it leads to smaller intercepts, also causes some complication compared to those methods which work all sights from a common Assumed (whole degree) Latitude.

76. USE OF CALCULATORS FOR THE SOLUTION OF SPHERICAL TRIANGLES.

Calculators are now available at a very reasonable cost and most students have been quick to take advantage of them to eliminate the tedium and increase the accuracy of mathematical calculations. The student will require a calculator which is capable of dealing with mathematical and trigonometric functions and the prices of these can vary a good deal. The main difference in the more expensive models, apart from quality, is that they have a number of memory stores, while the cheaper model will usually have only a single memory store.

It is generally agreed that a whole calculation should be done in the machine without having to record information externally part-way through the calculation. This aim is usually achieved in a multi-memory machine, but can often be achieved on a single memory machine if the formula is rearranged before commencing the calculation. The following example will serve to illustrate this point.

Example 1.

To find the third side of a spherical triangle, given two sides and included angle.

$$A = 88° \ 19' = 88°·316667$$
$$b = 100° \ 20' = 100°·333333$$
$$c = 98° \ 41·5' = 98°·691667$$

Using $\cos a = \cos b \ \cos c + \sin b \ \sin c \ \cos A$
the formula can be rearranged as
$\cos a = \cos b \ \cos c \ (1 + \tan b \ \tan c \ \cos A)$
when the single memory calculator can successfully complete the

operation. The programme may now be carried out, obtaining
$$a=86° ·80848=86° 48' 30·5''$$

Example 2.

To find any angle of a spherical triangle, given three sides.

$$a=70°$$
$$b=62°$$
$$c=46°$$

Using $\cos A = \dfrac{\cos a - \cos b \cos c}{\sin b \sin c}$ the calculator will deal with this

formula as it stands and the programme can be carried out giving
$$A=88° ·56572=88° 33' 57''.$$

EXERCISE 6.—MISCELLANEOUS EXAMPLES FOR REVISION.

The following examples illustrate applications of spherical trigonometry to problems of a somewhat more sophisticated type. The trigonometry required is entirely to be found within the pages of this book. In addition, however, a knowledge of mathematics, navigation and spherical astronomy is assumed up to approximately first or second year university standard or its equivalent. Answers given are in an extended form, where practicable, in order to provide guidance.

1. (i) Using the four-part formula, show that in the PZX astronavigational triangle, $C=B-A$,
     where $A=$tan lat. cot LHA
     $B=$tan decl. cosec LHA
     $C=$cot Z sec lat.

    (ii) Define 'amplitude' and prove that
     sin amp$=$sin decl. sec lat.

    (iii) Explain fully the uses of Tables based upon the formulae of (i) and (ii).

2. Define 'point of no return'.

    A vessel on a Great Circle track from A (5° 30' S., 35° 15' W.) to B (34° 50' S., 20° 00' W.) has sufficient fuel for the passage plus a reserve of 20%. Ignoring weather and current and assuming constant speed throughout in either direction, calculate the longitude of the point of no return.

3. By applying the sine formula to the astronomical triangle PZX show that the rate of change of azimuth may be given by
     $$\triangle Z=-15 (\sin θ-\tan A \cos Z \cos θ) \text{ minutes of arc}$$
     per minute of time,
     where $θ=$latitude
     $A=$altitude
     $Z=$azimuth

4. Show that for two places on the same parallel of latitude the least distance between them is less than the distance along the parallel by

$2 (\alpha \cos \theta - \sin^{-1} (\sin \alpha \cos \theta))$ cosec $1'$ nautical miles,

where θ is the latitude of the parallel and α is half the difference of longitude between the places.

Prove by appeal to the geometry of the sphere or otherwise that the value of this expression is always positive.

5. (i) To an observer in lat. $\theta°$ N., two stars, A and B of respective declinations α and β rise simultaneously. Later, A transits at the instant B sets. Prove that

$$\tan \theta \tan \alpha = 1 - 2 \tan^2 \theta \tan^2 \beta$$

(ii) Prove that to an observer in lat. $45°$ N. the interval between the instant when a rising star is on the prime vertical and the instant it sets is constant.

6. In the astro-navigation triangle PZX, if the co-latitude of an observer is C, prove that

$C = x + \cos^{-1} (\cos p \sec y)$ given that

$\tan x = \cot d \cos H$ and $\sin y = \cos d \sin H$, where d is declination, H is LHA and p is zenith distance.

Explain how these forms may be used to give a 'short method' solution of the PZX triangle.

7. What is the condition that a star should have a maximum azimuth?

Prove that the maximum azimuth A of a star of declination D as seen from latitude L is given by

$\sin A = \mp \cos D \sec L$ and give an explanation of the $\mp$ signs.

At latitude $45°$ N. the maximum azimuth of a certain star is $225°$ T. Find the declination of the star.

8. Define 'curve of constant bearing'. Show that the angle δ between a curve of constant bearing and a Great Circle bearing is given by

$$\tan \delta = \sin \varphi \tan \lambda$$

where φ is the latitude of the observing vessel and λ the difference of longitude between the vessel and the transmitter.

Explain how this knowledge may be used in practice.

9. A Cosmos satellite is launched from Archangel (A) ($63°$ N., $40°$ E.) in an easterly direction. After injection its orbital plane makes an angle of $66°$ with the equatorial plane and its period is $89·5$ minutes. If V is the northern vertex of the satellite's initial trajectory and B is the intersection of the trajectory with the parallel of latitude of $51°$ $30'$ N., find the

position of the vertex, V the time taken by the satellite in travelling from B to A and from A to B.

10. Deduce formulae which transform equatorial co-ordinates α and δ of a heavenly body X into ecliptic co-ordinates λ and β, the obliquity of the ecliptic being ε. How are these formulae simplified when applied to the sun?

Find the ecliptic co-ordinates of the star Aldebaran $(\alpha=\text{04h 34m 24s}, \delta=+16° 27')$. Take $\varepsilon=23° 27'$.

Does this star lie within the Zodiac?

11. Show that the angle between a curve of constant bearing and a Great Circle bearing is given by
$$\tan (\beta-\alpha)=\sin \varphi \tan \lambda$$
where $(\beta-\alpha)$ is the angle required for a position in latitude φ, longitude $(x+\lambda)$ and the observed Great Circle bearing of a radio transmitter in latitude φ_2 longitude x is α.

12. If the stars Alioth and Vega were simultaneously at maximum azimuths on opposite sides of the meridian, what was the observer's latitude?

	Declination	S.H.A.
Alioth	56° 10′ N.	167° 00′
Vega	38° 45′ N.	81° 00′

13. (i) In the astronomical triangle PZX, show that the rate of change of altitude (A) is given by
$$|\triangle A|=15' \cos \varphi \sin Z \text{ per minute of time,}$$
in which $\varphi=$latitude and $Z=$azimuth.

(ii) Two stars have Right Ascensions which differ by 12 hours. Their declinations are equal in magnitude but of opposite names. Show that at any instant, at any given place, their rates of change of altitude are numerically equal.

14. (i) Prove that, if the maximum azimuth of a circumpolar star is 45° to an observer in latitude 45° N., the declination of the star is 60° N.

(ii) If the declination δ of a star is greater than the latitude φ of an observer, prove that the star's greatest azimuth east or west is sin ($\cos \delta \sec \varphi$).

APPENDIX

Plane trigonometry—some useful formulae.

In writing this book on spherical trigonometry it has been necessary to assume that the reader already has a sound working knowledge of plane trigonometry.

Even so, in this Appendix we propose to give a summary of those formulae of plane trigonometry which have particular importance in the various proofs and applications of spherical trigonometry. They are given without proof and the student who wishes to go more deeply into them will have no difficulty in finding several good text books available on the subject.

Throughout this book, we shall occasionally, where helpful, refer to these formulae by means of the numbering given at the side. Thus, "using A.12," for instance, is taken to mean "using formula number 12 from Appendix."

Summary.

1.
$$\left. \begin{array}{l} \sin^2 A + \cos^2 A = 1 \\ \sec^2 A - \tan^2 A = 1 \\ \operatorname{cosec}^2 A - \cot^2 A = 1 \end{array} \right\} \quad .. \qquad .. \qquad .. \qquad .. \quad A.1$$

2.
$$\tan A = \frac{\sin A}{\cos A} \text{ and } \cot A = \frac{\cos A}{\sin A} \qquad .. \qquad .. \quad A.2$$

3. In the second quadrant, i.e. angles from 90° to 180°, only the sine and cosec are +ve. All others are −ve. Thus:—

$$\begin{array}{ll} \sin & (90°+A) = \cos A \\ \operatorname{cosec} & (90°+A) = \sec A \\ \text{but} \quad \cos & (90°+A) = -\sin A \\ \tan & (90°+A) = -\cot A \\ \sec & (90°+A) = -\operatorname{cosec} A \\ \cot & (90°+A) = -\tan A \end{array} \qquad \begin{array}{ll} \sin & (180°-A) = \sin A \\ \operatorname{cosec} & (180°-A) = \operatorname{cosec} A \\ \text{but} \quad \cos & (180°-A) = -\cos A \\ \tan & (180°-A) = -\tan A \\ \sec & (180°-A) = -\sec A \\ \cot & (180°-A) = -\cot A \end{array}$$

$$.. \; A.3$$

Also remember, $\sin 90° = 1$ and $\cos 90° = 0$

4. Compound angles.
$$\sin (A+B) = \sin A \cos B + \cos A \sin B$$
$$\sin (A-B) = \sin A \cos B - \cos A \sin B \qquad .. \qquad .. \qquad .. \qquad .. \quad A.4$$

5. $\cos (A+B) = \cos A \cos B - \sin A \sin B$
$$\cos (A-B) = \cos A \cos B + \sin A \sin B \qquad .. \qquad .. \qquad .. \qquad .. \quad A.5$$

6. $\tan (A+B) = \dfrac{\tan A + \tan B}{1 - \tan A \tan B}$

$$\tan (A-B) = \frac{\tan A - \tan B}{1 + \tan A \tan B} \qquad .. \qquad .. \qquad .. \qquad .. \qquad .. \quad A.6$$

7. Functions of $2A$.
$$\sin 2A = 2 \sin A \cos A$$
$$\cos 2A = \cos^2 A - \sin^2 A$$
$$\tan 2A = \frac{2 \tan A}{1 - \tan^2 A} \quad .. \qquad .. \qquad .. \qquad .. \qquad .. \qquad .. \qquad .. \quad A.7$$

8. Transformation of sums into products.
$\sin A + \sin B = 2 \sin \frac{1}{2} (A+B) \cos \frac{1}{2} (A-B)$
In words:—twice sine half sum cos half difference
$\sin A - \sin B = 2 \cos \frac{1}{2} (A+B) \sin \frac{1}{2} (A-B)$
In words:—twice cos half sum sine half difference
$\cos A + \cos B = 2 \cos \frac{1}{2} (A+B) \cos \frac{1}{2} (A-B)$
In words:—twice cos half sum cos half difference
$\cos A - \cos B = 2 \sin \frac{1}{2} (A+B) \sin \frac{1}{2} (B-A)$
In words:—twice sine half sum sine half difference reversed $\qquad .. \quad A.8$

9. Products into sums.
   Conversely:—
   2 sin A cos B=sine sum+sine difference.
   2 cos A sin B=sine sum−sine difference
   2 cos A cos B=cos sum+cos difference
   2 sin A sin B=cos difference−cos sum

   .. .. A.9

10. Functions of 3 A.
    sin 3 A=3 sin A−4 sin³ A
    cos 3 A=4 cos³ A−3 cos A

    $$\tan 3\ A = \frac{3 \tan A - \tan^3 A}{1 - 3 \tan^2 A}$$

    .. .. A.10

11. Two useful formulae.

    $$2 \sin^2 \frac{A}{2} = 1 - \cos A$$

    $$2 \cos^2 \frac{A}{2} = 1 + \cos A$$ A.11

12. Cosine formula.
    In any plane triangle ABC,
    $a^2 = b^2 + c^2 - 2\ b\ c \cos A$ A.12

13. Area of triangle ABC=½ $b\ c$ sin A
    Area of triangle $ABC = \sqrt{s\ (s-a)\ (s-b)\ (s-c)}$, where
    $s = \frac{1}{2}(a+b+c)$ A.13

14. From 13,
    $\frac{1}{2}\ b\ c$ sin $A = \sqrt{s\ (s-a)\ (s-b)\ (s-c)}$

    i.e. $\sin A = \frac{2}{bc}\ \sqrt{s\ (s-a)\ (s-b)\ (s-c)}$

    By putting $s = \frac{a}{2} + \frac{b}{2} + \frac{c}{2}$

    $s-a = \frac{b}{2} + \frac{c}{2} - \frac{a}{2}$

    $s-b = \frac{a}{2} + \frac{c}{2} - \frac{b}{2}$

    $s-c = \frac{a}{2} + \frac{b}{2} - \frac{c}{2}$ and multiplying up, we get

    $\sin A = \frac{1}{2\ b\ c}\ \sqrt{2a^2b^2 + 2b^2c^2 + 2c^2a^2 - a^4 - b^4 - c^4}$

    .. .. A.14

15. If θ is in radians, then

    $\sin \theta = \theta - \frac{\theta^3}{3!} + \frac{\theta^5}{5!} -$

    $\cos \theta = 1 - \frac{\theta^2}{2!} + \frac{\theta^4}{4!} -$

    .. .. A.15

16. For expressing angles in minutes of arc instead of radians, or conversely, remember that
    θ (minutes)=θ (radians)×sin 1′
    Also if θ is a *small* angle in radians, then sin θ=θ and tan θ=θ.
    .. .. A.16

Exercise 1. Oblique triangles.

1. $b=83°\ 00'$, $p=71°\ 00'$
2. $p=64°\ 00'$, $z=85°\ 00'$
3. $p=126°\ 59'·5$, $z=56°\ 04'·5$
4. $P=81°\ 24'$, $Z=61°\ 32'$
5. $p=87°\ 01'$, $Z=97°\ 46'$

6. $B=31°\ 34'$
7. $PX=92°\ 07'$, $ZX=58°\ 31'$
8. $A=59°\ 01'$, $B=74°\ 52'$.
9. $Z=100°\ 30'$
10. $a=101°\ 26'·5$, $b=123°\ 23'$.

Exercise 2. Right angled triangles.

1. $b=60°\ 10'$, $c=100°\ 00'$, $C=98°\ 42'$
2. $a=112°\ 27'$, $p=85°\ 17'$, $b=102°\ 26'$.
3. $Y=45°\ 06'$, $Z=114°\ 26'·5$, $z=107°\ 51'$.
4. $C=49°\ 32'$, $c=50°\ 46'$, $b=77°\ 02'$
5. $P=53°\ 21'·5$, $x=92°\ 36'$, $y=91°\ 33'$.
6. $042°\ 37'$ T., D. Long. $22°\ 51'$.
7. Lat. $45°\ 00'$ N.
8. $241°\ 12'$ T., 1358 mls.
9. Lat. $30°\ 31'$ S.
10. Lat. $40°\ 28·5'$ S.
11. (a) 4105 mls., (b) Lat. $30°\ 53'$ S.
12. B. Lat. $10°\ 00'$ S. A. Lat. $29°\ 50'$ N.

Exercise 3. Problems.

1. $85°\ 53'$.
2. $72°$.
3. 206·6 sq. in.
4. $89°\ 33'·7$
5. $23·32°$, $46·64°$, $116·59°$.
6. 452·6 sq. in.
7. A, $6°\ 59'·7$ N.: B, $33°\ 00'$ N.
8. $24°\ 34'$ E.
9. Decl. $21°\ 04'$ N. Cel. lat. $00°$ $00'$. Cel. long. $64°\ 33'$
10. $42°\ 56'$ N., $4°\ 36'$ E.
11. R.A. 02h 59m 37s. Decl. $21°$ $27'·8$ N.
12. $30°\ 03'·5$.
13. L.H.A. $290°\ 44'$. Alt. $30°\ 54'·5$.
14. $46°\ 06'·7$ N., $234°\ 34'·7$.
15. $15°\ 02'$.
16. $59°\ 22'$ N.
17. $18°\ 08'$., N$74°\ 29'$ W.
18. L.H.A. $262°\ 21'$.
19. $29°\ 40'$ N.
20. $24°\ 08'$.
21. Lat. $10°\ 07'·5$ S.
22. Lat. $27°\ 00'$ N., Long. $035°\ 00'$.
23. Lat. $42°\ 00'·5$, Decl. $22°\ 48'·5$.
24. Lat. $59°\ 11'$ N.

25. Lat. $47°\ 37'$.
26. Lat. $32°\ 04'$ S.
27. Lat. $46°\ 46'$ N., Decl. $20°\ 02'$ N.
28. Lat. $48°\ 00'$ N.
29. Lat. $34°\ 58'$ S. or $55°\ 02'$ S.
30. N. $77°\ 54'$ E., 09h 52m 08s.
31. Lat. $61°\ 14'$ S.
32. Lat. $47°\ 56'$, Decl. $20°\ 02'$.
33. Lat. $45°\ 00'$ N.
34. Lat. $38°\ 59'$ N.
35. S.H.A. $197°\ 14'$.
36. Long. $29°\ 14'$ W. or $19°\ 51'$ E.
37. Decl. $17°\ 35'$ N.
38. Lat. $49°\ 11'$ N., Decl. $20°\ 57'$ N.
39. 624 miles.
40. 3438 miles (±20)
41. Lat. $40°\ 04'$, Decl. $15°\ 46'$.
42. A and B, $27°\ 36'$ S., C, $51°\ 27'$ S.
43. Lat. $58°\ 55'$ S.
44. Decl. $19°\ 44'$ S.
45. R.A. 11h 53m 50s.
46. Long. $95°\ 34'$ E.
47. Decl. $48°\ 10'$ S.
48. D. Long. $77°\ 27'$.
49. Lat. $23°\ 32'$ N.
50. Decl. $5°\ 33'$ S.

Exercise 4.

1. $156°$.

Exercise 6.

2. That point from which it is theoretically just possible to return to starting point using all fuel on board.
   If K is the P.N.R., then $AK = 60\%$ of AB.
   $AB = 1952 \cdot 5$ mls., $A = 23° \, 40 \cdot 2'$, Long. $K = 26° \, 51'$ W.

7. Show that in general $|D| > |L|$ applies; $\mp$ signs take account of the PZX triangle W. or E. of the meridian, respectively; $D = \pm 60°$, the —ve value being valid in this case.

9. Long. vertex $= 69° \, 06'$ E. and by inspection, its latitude is $66°$ N., Long. of $B = 13° \, 08'$ E., $BA = 18° \, 18'$, time B to $A = 4 \cdot 55$ mins. from which it follows that from A to B time $= 84 \cdot 95$ mins.

10. If P is the pole of the equator, K the pole of the ecliptic, then in triangle PZX we can obtain
    $$\sin \beta = \cos \varepsilon \sin \delta - \sin \varepsilon \cos \delta \sin \alpha$$
    and $\cos \alpha \tan \lambda = \sin \varepsilon \tan \delta + \cos \varepsilon \sin \alpha$
    For the sun $\beta = $ zero and we can derive $\sin \lambda = \sin \delta \operatorname{cosec} \varepsilon$.
    For Aldebaran, $\beta = -5° \, 21'$, $\lambda = 69° \, 25'$. For the Zodiac, must have $|\beta| < 8°$; Aldebaran lies within the Zodiac.

12. Lat. $36°$ N.